Meet MINITAB

Release 13

for Windows®

Windows® 95/98/2000 and Windows NT™

February 2000

ISBN 0-925636-42-8
© 1999 by Minitab Inc. All rights reserved.

Printed in the USA
Revised Printing, 12/00
✪ Text and cover printed on recycled paper.

MINITAB is a U.S. registered trademark of Minitab Inc. Other brands or product names are trademarks or registered trademarks of their respective holders.

LICENSE AGREEMENT FOR MINITAB™ FOR WINDOWS®

IMPORTANT - READ CAREFULLY: This is a legal agreement between "You" (either an individual or single legal entity) and Minitab Inc. governing the use of the software product identified above ("Software"). By opening the sealed package containing the Software, you agree to the terms of this Agreement. If you do not agree to these terms, you should promptly return the *unopened* Software package to the place of purchase for a full refund, or contact Minitab Inc.

The type of license offered you by this Agreement (for "annual" or "perpetual" use) is listed on the back of the media sleeve (for Software supplied on CD-ROM) or on the Disk #1 label (if supplied on 3.5" disks).

A. Terms and Conditions Applicable to Perpetual Use Licenses
   - You are granted a license to use this Software in perpetuity, subject to the terms, fees, conditions, restrictions, and limitations contained herein and on the applicable Minitab Price List.
   - This Software may be used on any compatible computer, even if attached to a network, provided that the Software is used on only one computer and by one user at a time.
   - Minitab Inc. will provide reasonable amounts of technical support to Registered Users for so long as this Software is generally distributed by Minitab Inc. to customers, and for one (1) year thereafter.

B. Terms and Conditions Applicable to Annual Use Licenses
   - You are granted a license to use this Software for a period of one year, subject to the terms, fees, conditions, restrictions and limitations contained herein and on the applicable Minitab Price List.
   - The annual license fee from our then-current Price List governs the number of users permitted to use this Software. The number of licensed users of the Software may be increased during the term(s) of this license by paying additional user fees for the time remaining in your then-current license term.
   - This license may be renewed for additional one-year terms by paying the then-current annual license fee. All terms and conditions of this Agreement will apply during the renewal term(s).
   - Minitab Inc. will provide routine maintenance to Registered Users during the term(s) of the license, including reasonable amounts of technical support and all program updates and new releases of the Software as they become available.

C. Terms and Conditions Applicable to Both Perpetual and Annual Use Licenses
   - This Agreement will be governed under the laws of the Commonwealth of Pennsylvania, USA.
   - You may make copies of the Software for each licensed user and for archival and back-up purposes.
   - Minitab Inc. may terminate this license for material breach by you. Upon termination, you agree to stop using, and to destroy all copies of, the Software licensed hereunder.
   - You may not disassemble, de-compile, or reverse engineer this Software in any way.
   - This Software license may not be assigned or otherwise transferred to another without our written permission.
   - This Software may not be exported without the appropriate export license.
   - All license fees are exclusive of any tariffs, duties, or taxes imposed or levied by a government or governmental agency.
   - The Software is the property of Minitab Inc. or its licensors and is protected by United States copyright laws and international treaties.
   - This Software and its documentation are provided to the U.S. Federal Government under RESTRICTED RIGHTS. Use, duplication, or disclosure by the Government is subject to restrictions as set forth in subparagraph (c)(1)(ii) of the Rights in Technical Data and Computer Software clause at DFARS 252.227-7013 or subparagraphs (c)(1) and (2) of the Commercial Computer Software - Restricted Rights at 48 CFR 52.227-19, as applicable. Manufacturer is Minitab Inc., 3081 Enterprise Drive, State College, Pennsylvania 16801.
   - The terms of this License Agreement do not apply if this Software has been furnished to you pursuant to a separate, written license agreement executed by both parties.

LIMITED WARRANTY

Minitab Inc. warrants that we have the right to grant this License to use this Software and that the functions contained in this Software will operate without substantial program errors. In the event of a breach of the above warranties, you will be entitled to a refund of all sums paid by you for the right to use this Software during that license term, as your sole and exclusive remedy for such breach. This Software is provided under this Agreement AS IS, without warranty of any kind except as set forth above. ALL IMPLIED WARRANTIES OF MERCHANTABILITY OR FITNESS FOR A PARTICULAR PURPOSE ARE EXPRESSLY DISCLAIMED. IN NO EVENT SHALL MINITAB, INC., ITS SUBSIDIARIES, DISTRIBUTORS, AGENTS, COMMISSIONAIRES, SERVICE PROVIDERS, OR MARKETING REPRESENTATIVES BE LIABLE TO YOU OR ANY OTHER PARTY FOR ANY LOSS OR DAMAGE, CONSEQUENTIAL, INDIRECT, SPECIAL, INCIDENTAL OR OTHERWISE ARISING FROM THE USE OF THIS SOFTWARE.

Some jurisdictions do not allow the limitation or exclusion of liability for incidental or consequential damages so the above limitation may not apply to you.

February 2000

Table of Contents

Welcome to MINITAB for Windows 95/98 and NT

MINITAB Release 13 is a powerful statistical software package that provides a wide range of data analysis and graphics capabilities; intuitive user interface; clean, clear output; procedure-specific statistical guidance; and extensive, context-sensitive online help. Whether used in industry, research, or teaching, MINITAB offers the ideal combination of power, accuracy, and ease of use to help you do your job better.

Earlier releases of MINITAB are available for Windows 3.1, Macintosh/Power Macintosh, and DOS microcomputers, and most of the leading workstations, minicomputers, and mainframe computers. Contact us at the address on the back of this book for details.

At a glance, MINITAB Release 13 offers you the following:

- Comprehensive statistics capabilities, including exploratory data analysis, basic statistics, regression, analysis of variance, sample size and power calculations, multivariate analysis, nonparametrics, time series, cross-tabulations, and simulations and distributions.

- StatGuide—Statistical guidance for many of MINITAB's text-based and graphical analyses—from basic statistics, to quality assurance, to design of experiments—so you get the most from your data analysis efforts.

- High-resolution graphics that are presentation-quality, fully editable, and include a brushing capability for identifying points on plots and pinpointing the actual data point in the Data window. Paste graphs into other applications and edit them via OLE.

- Quality assurance and improvement features, including
  - Run charts, Pareto charts, and cause-and-effect (fishbone) diagrams
  - Statistical process control charts
  - Historical charts
  - Capability analysis
  - Measurement systems analysis with Gage R&R
  - Design of experiments capabilities to generate and analyze full and fractional designs, Plackett-Burman designs, Taguchi designs, response surface designs, and mixture models
  - Multiple response optimization
  - Estimation of failure time distributions
  - Regression with life data and accelerated life testing

- Powerful data management capabilities. Import data from other versions of MINITAB, spreadsheets, databases, and text files into a project. Link data to another application or another part of a MINITAB worksheet using Dynamic Data Exchange (DDE). Share data with your database using Open Database Connectivity (ODBC). Easily create subsets of your data.

- Project Manager. Minitab's Project Manager provides easy access to all the components of your MINITAB project. You can rename worksheet columns and add columns descriptions; browse through your worksheets, graphs, and output; organize related documents and URLs; and more.

- ReportPad. A tool integrated into the Project Manager that helps you generate a report from your analysis.

- A macro facility that allows you to write a program of MINITAB commands to automate repetitive tasks or to extend MINITAB's functionality.

- A graphical interface that provides an easy-to-use, efficient work environment.

- Online tutorials. The same tutorials available in *Meet MINITAB* are now available in the Help menu.

How to Use *Meet MINITAB*

This book is not designed to be read from cover to cover. It is designed to provide you with quick access to the information you need. If it fails to meet that objective, please let us know in any way you find convenient, including sending e-mail to doc_comments@minitab.com.

Whether you are a new or a long-time MINITAB user, you should be sure to review the information in Chapter 1, *MINITAB Essentials*. There are some important new features—such as the Project Manager, ReportPad, and AutoFill—and this is an excellent introduction.

This book provides introductory and overview information to help you get "up and running" quickly, including several sample sessions.

The *MINITAB User's Guide 1: Data, Graphics, and Macros* provides reference information on the following topics:

- data
- file I/O
- graphics
- macros

The *MINITAB User's Guide 2: Data Analysis and Quality Tools* provides reference information on the following topics:

- statistics
- quality control
- reliability and survival analysis
- design of experiments

Assumptions

This guide assumes that you know the basics of using your operating system (such as Windows 95, Windows 98, or Windows NT). This includes using menus, dialog boxes, a mouse, and moving and resizing windows. If you are not familiar with these operations, see your operating system documentation.

Register as a MINITAB User

Please send us your MINITAB registration card. If you have lost or misplaced your registration card, contact your distributor, Minitab Ltd., Minitab SARL, or Minitab Inc. Please refer to the back cover of this guide or the *International Partners Card* included in your software product box for contact information. You can also register via the world wide web at http://www.minitab.com.

Registered MINITAB users are eligible to receive free technical support (subject to the terms and conditions of their License Agreement), new product announcements, maintenance updates, and MINITAB newsletters containing useful articles, tips, and macro information.

Global Support

Minitab Inc. and its international subsidiaries and partners provide sales and support services to Minitab customers throughout the world. Please refer to the *International Partners Card* included in your software product box. You can also access the most up-to-date international partner information via our web site at http://www.minitab.com.

Customer Support

For technical help, contact your central computing support group if one exists. You may also be eligible to receive customer support from your distributor, or from Minitab Inc., Minitab Ltd., or Minitab SARL directly, subject to the terms and conditions of your License Agreement. Eligible users may contact their distributor, Minitab Ltd., Minitab SARL, or Minitab Inc. (phone 814-231-2MTB (2682), fax 814-238-4383, or send e-mail through our web site at http://www.minitab.com/contacts). Technical support at Minitab Inc. is available Monday through Friday, between the hours of 9:00 a.m. and 5:00 p.m. Eastern time. When you are calling for technical support, it is helpful if you can be at your computer when you call. Please have your serial and software version numbers handy (from the **Help ➤ About MINITAB** screen), along with a detailed description of the problem.

Troubleshooting information is provided in a file called ReadMe.txt, installed in the main MINITAB directory, and in Help under the topics *Troubleshooting* and *How Do I*.... You can also visit the Support section of our web site at http://www.minitab.com/support.

MINITAB on the Internet

Visit our web site at http://www.minitab.com. You can download demos, macros, and maintenance updates, get the latest information about our company and its products, get help from our technical support specialists, and more.

About the Documentation

Printed MINITAB documentation provides menu and dialog box documentation only. You'll find step-by-step "how-to's" throughout the books. (You'll find complete session command documentation available via online Help.)

MINITAB's new StatGuide provides you with statistical guidance for many analyses, so you get the most from your data analysis. Chapter overviews, particularly in *User's Guide 2*, provide additional statistical guidance to help determine suitability of a particular method. Many examples in both printed documentation and online Help include *Interpreting your output*.

The software itself provides online Help, a convenient, comprehensive, and useful source of information. To help you use MINITAB most effectively, Minitab Inc. and other publishers offer a variety of helpful texts and documents.

To order from Minitab Inc. from within the U.S. or Canada call: 800-448-3555. Additional contact information for Minitab Inc., Minitab Ltd., and Minitab SARL is given on the back cover of this book.

Documentation for MINITAB for Windows, Release 13

MINITAB Help, ©2000, Minitab Inc. This comprehensive, convenient source of information is available at the touch of a key or the click of the mouse. In addition to complete menu and dialog box documentation, you can find overviews, examples, guidance for setting up your data, information on calculations and methods, and a glossary. A separate online Help file is available for session commands.

MINITAB StatGuide, ©2000, Minitab Inc. Statistical guidance for many of MINITAB's text-based and graphical analyses—from basic statistics, to quality assurance, to design of experiments—so you get the most from your data analysis efforts. The MINITAB StatGuide uses preselected examples to help you understand and interpret output.

Meet MINITAB, ©2000, Minitab Inc. Rather than fully document all features, this book explains the fundamentals of using MINITAB—how to use the menus and dialog boxes, how to manage and manipulate data and files, how to produce graphs, and more. This guide includes five step-by-step sample sessions to help you learn MINITAB quickly.

MINITAB User's Guide 1: Data, Graphics, and Macros, ©2000, Minitab Inc. This guide includes how to use MINITAB's input, output, and data manipulation capabilities; how to work with data and graphs; and how to write macros.

MINITAB User's Guide 2: Data Analysis and Quality Tools, ©2000, Minitab Inc. This guide includes how to use MINITAB's statistics, quality control, reliability and survival analysis, and design of experiments tools.

Online tutorials. The same tutorials available in *Meet MINITAB*, designed to help new users learn MINITAB, are now available in the Help menu.

Session Command Quick Reference, ©2000, Minitab Inc. A Portable Document Format (PDF) file, to be read with Acrobat Reader, that lists all MINITAB commands and subcommands.

The CD-ROM distribution of MINITAB Release 13 includes our printed documentation—*Meet MINITAB*, *MINITAB User's Guide 1*, and *MINITAB User's Guide 2*—in Portable Document Format (PDF) files along with the Acrobat Reader for you to use these publications electronically. You may view them online with the Reader, or print portions of particular interest to you.

Related Documentation

Companion Text List, 1996, Minitab Inc., State College, PA. More than 300 textbooks, textbook supplements, and other related teaching materials that include MINITAB are featured in the *Companion Text List*. For a complete bibliography, the *Companion Text List* is available online at http://www.minitab.com.

MINITAB Handbook, Third Edition, 1994, Barbara F. Ryan, and Brian L. Joiner, Duxbury Press, Belmont, CA. A supplementary text that teaches basic statistics using MINITAB. The Handbook features the creative use of plots, application of standard statistical methods to real data, in-depth exploration of data, simulation as a learning tool, screening data for errors, manipulating data, transformation of data, and performing multiple regressions. Please contact your bookstore, Minitab Inc., or Duxbury Press to order this book.

Typographical Conventions Used in this Book

C	denotes a column, such as C12 or 'Height'.
K	denotes a constant, such as 8.3 or K14.
M	denotes a matrix, such as M5.
[Enter]	denotes a key, such as the Enter key.
[Alt]+[D]	denotes pressing the second key while holding down the first key. For example, while holding down the [Alt] key, press the [D] key.
File ➤ Exit	denotes a menu command, such as choose Exit from the File menu. Here is another example: **Stat ➤ Tables ➤ Tally** means open the Stat menu, then open the Tables submenu, then choose Tally.
Click **OK**.	Bold text also clarifies dialog box items and buttons.
Enter *Pulse1*.	Italic text specifies text to be entered by you.

Sample Data Sets

For some examples you need to type data into columns. But for most examples, you can use data already stored in sample data set files in the DATA subdirectory of the main MINITAB directory.

MINITAB comes with a number of sample data sets that are stored in the DATA, STUDENT1, STUDENT8, STUDENT9, and STUDNT12 subdirectories (folders). For complete descriptions of most of these data sets, see the Help topic *sample data sets*.

Release 13 Capabilities Summary

◆ = New Release 13 capability

General

- Menu interface, command-line option
- One CD-ROM runs on: Windows NT or Windows 95/98
- Easy-to-use manuals and Help
- ◆ StatGuide explains how to interpret statistical tables and graphs in a practical, easy-to-understand way
- Documentation helps you analyze your data using MINITAB and interpret your results
- Powerful macro programming language
- Dynamic worksheet size
- ◆ Worksheet allows up to 4000 columns
- Session window: edit; paste output into word processor with formatting intact; save output in RTF format
- ◆ ReportPad: easily generate a report from your project work
- 32-bit processing for faster speed
- Variable names can be up to 31 characters
- Context-sensitive right-click pop-up menus, detachable toolbars, and a status bar
- ◆ Online tutorials

Data and File Management

- ◆ Project Manager: browse through MINITAB windows with a tree-like navigator; organize and manage different worksheets, windows, and files
- Multiple worksheets
- Import/Export: Excel, Lotus 1-2-3, Quattro Pro, dBASE, and text files
- Preview any worksheet file before importing

- Import date and time data: use it in graphs, for subsetting, and for analyses
- Calculator
- DDE (Dynamic Data Exchange)
- Spreadsheet-like Data window for entering and editing data
- ◆ Use Autofill to automatically fill Data window cells with patterned data values by dragging your mouse
- ◆ Clipboard replications in the Data window
- Insert and move columns in the Data window
- ◆ Hide and unhide columns in the Data window
- Specify the order in which you would like text categories processed by MINITAB commands
- Data manipulation: merge, stack, subset, sort, recode
- ◆ Merge worksheets based on common variables in a specified column so all rows are synchronized
- ◆ Improved stack and unstack: put data in a new worksheet; more useful subscript names
- ◆ Switch columns to rows or rows to columns easily
- Create new worksheets easily with data subsetting
- ◆ Find and Replace in Data window
- Font control in Data window
- Store descriptive information with a project
- ◆ Paste with existing column names: MINITAB resolves the conflict
- Save graphs, worksheets, and session output in one file
- Matrix functions including transpose, inverse, eigenvalues, eigenvectors

- ODBC (Open DataBase Connectivity) to query and retrieve data from databases
- Use numeric, text, and date/time data for categorical variables in analyses, such as ANOVA, DOE, and tables
- Double-precision worksheets

Basic Statistics

- Descriptive statistics, with both numerical and graphical summaries
- Store descriptive statistics easily
- Confidence intervals, one- and two-sample t-tests, paired t-tests
- Paired t-test and t-interval
- Estimation and tests for 1 and 2 proportion problems
- Correlation and covariance matrices
- p-values for correlation
- Normality test
- Two variances: test for equal variances

Regression Analysis

- Simple and multiple linear regression
- Model selection using stepwise or best subsets regression
- ◆ Stepwise regression: new option for backward/forward selection procedures
- Plot the regression line with confidence and prediction bands
- Identification of unusual observations, model diagnostics, prediction/confidence intervals for new observations
- Residual plots
- Logistic regression: binary, ordinal, or nominal; diagnostic plots
- Polynomial regression, with or without log transforms

Analysis of Variance

- General linear model for balanced and unbalanced designs
- Unbalanced nested designs for analyzing a wider range of experimental designs
- Analysis of Means
- Multiple factor ANOVA for balanced models, fixed and random effects
- Analyze fully nested designs
- Multiple comparisons
- Expected mean squares, approximate F tests
- Sequential and adjusted sums of squares, identification of unusual observations, model diagnostics
- Residual, main effects, and interaction plots
- Tests of homogeneity of variances

Multivariate Analysis

- Principal component analysis
- Discriminant analysis
- Cluster analysis
- Factor analysis
- Multivariate analysis of variance

Tables

- Simple and multiple correspondence analysis
- Cross-tabulations
- Contingency tables
- Goodness-of-fit test

Statistical Process Control

- Run chart
- Pareto chart
- Fishbone diagram
- Control charts: XBar, R, S, XBar-R, XBar-S, I, MR, I-MR, I-MR-R/S, MA,

EWMA, CUSUM, zone, short run, p, np, c, u

- Use normal or non-normal data with variables control charts
- Customizable tests for special causes
- Historical charts that estimate central limits and center line independently for different groups on the same chart
- Process capability analysis for normal and non-normal data, and attributes data
- ◆ Process capability analysis for batch data: takes into account within-group variation in addition to between-group
- ◆ Process capability analysis: selected terminology has been changed in response to user feedback
- Process Capability Sixpack for normal and Weibull data, which provides a visual display of process capability, verifies process stability, and checks that data are normal (or Weibull)
- Process Capability Sixpack for batch data
- Shainin Multi-Vari charts for graphical analysis of variance
- Normal and Weibull probability plots
- Symmetry plot
- Box-Cox transformation for non-normal data
- Gage R&R: ANOVA and XBar-R methods, gage linearity and accuracy; gage run chart
- ◆ Nested Gage R&R
- ◆ Gage R&R: minor terminology changes and more useful layout of graphs in response to user feedback

Reliability and Survival Analysis

- Parametric distribution analysis using eight common lifetime distributions
- ◆ Parametric distribution analysis: test shape parameters against historical values; compare distribution parameters for two or more samples
- ◆ Distribution fitting: goodness-of-fit measures for how well a distribution fits the data
- ◆ Least squares estimation method
- Nonparametric distribution analysis, including Kaplan-Meier, Actuarial, and Turnbull estimates
- Exact failure, right-, left-, and interval-censored data
- Accelerated life testing to perform a simple regression with one predictor
- ◆ Probability plot: based on fitted accelerated life testing model or based on individual fits at each level of the accelerating variable
- Regression with life data to investigate the relationship between failure time and one or more predictors
- ◆ Bayes analysis: handles cases with no failures
- ◆ Hypothesis tests on distribution parameters
- Probit analysis to estimate a stress distribution
- Plots: Distribution ID, Distribution Overview, Probability, Hazard, and Survival
- ◆ Distribution ID Plot and Distribution Overview Plot for arbitrarily censored data
- ◆ Confidence intervals for MTTF, standard deviation, and interquartile range; one-side confidence intervals

Designed Experiments

- DOE interface guides you through analysis
- Factorial designs: two-level full and fractional factorial design for 3 to 15 factors

- Create and analyze general full factorial designs
- Analyze factorial designs with botched runs
- ◆ Factorial designs: multiple response optimization, overlaid contour plot, contour/surface plots
- Plackett-Burman screening design for 3 to 47 factors
- Response surface designs: central composite, Box-Behnken, response surface regression
- Response surface contour, and wire frame plots
- Multiple response optimization: numerical, interactive graph, and overlaid contour plot
- ◆ Improved algorithm allows MINITAB to achieve the optimal solution more often than the previous release
- Mixture designs: simplex centroid and simplex lattice designs, fit Scheffé mixture models up to a full cubic
- ◆ Mixture designs: a powerful capability for creating and analyzing mixture designs; includes constraints on mixtures, process variables, and amounts
- ◆ Mixture designs: graphs to help you visualize your experiment including simplex design plots, trace plots, and contour/surface plots
- ◆ Mixture designs: multiple response optimization and overlaid contour plot
- ◆ Optimal designs: help you select the design points based on D-optimality, or distrance-based optimality criteria for a response surface or a mixtures design
- Easily modify or update existing experimental designs created in MINITAB
- Create user-specified designs
- Residual, main effects, interaction, and cube plots

- ◆ Taguchi designs: complete capability for generating and analyzing Taguchi (robust) designs; handles designs from L4 to L54; calculates signal-to-noise ratios; can accommodate static and dynamic analyses; predict results; plus much more

Sample Size and Power Calculations

- 1-sample Z, t, and proportion
- 2-sample t and proportion
- One-way ANOVA, 2-level factorial designs, and Plackett-Burman designs
- ◆ Solve for the number of center points for factorial and Plackett-Burman designs
- ◆ Provide any two of: power, difference, and sample size; MINITAB will solve for the third

Graphics

- Presentation-style graphics
- Scatter plots, box plots, histograms, charts, time series plots, 3D graphs
- Numerous special-purpose graphs
- Built-in graphs in analysis commands
- ◆ Probability plots: added least squares estimation method; plots now include two goodness-of-fit measures (Anderson-Darling statistic and Pearson correlation coefficient) to help assess how well the distribution fits your data
- High-resolution dotplot
- Ability to customize all attributes of every element in your graph: color, type size, fonts, data display, and annotation
- Powerful, easy-to-use graph editor
- OLE: edit MINITAB graphs in other applications
- Graph brushing: displays values of user-selected points on plot, points are

highlighted in all relevant graphs, and in Data window

- Subset and analyze data, based on brushed points
- Save graphs in TIFF, JPEG, PNG, and bitmap file formats

Time Series Analysis

- Autocorrelations, partial autocorrelations, and cross correlations
- Univariate Box-Jenkins ARIMA analysis: seasonal and nonseasonal with forecasts
- Trend analysis: linear, quadratic, exponential, or S-curve
- Decomposition: multiplicative or additive models
- Single or double exponential smoothing
- Winter's additive and multiplicative methods for exponential seasonal smoothing
- Moving average

Nonparametrics

- Sign test and confidence interval
- Wilcoxon test and confidence interval
- Mann-Whitney test and confidence interval
- Kruskal-Wallis test
- Friedman test for two-way layout
- Runs test
- Mood median test

Simulation and Distributions

- Random number generator: binomial, Poisson, normal, Weibull, beta, exponential, and logarithmic
- Density, distribution, and inverse cumulative distribution functions
- Random sampling, with or without replacement

1

MINITAB Essentials

Before You Start

What you should know before you begin

This guide, as well as the other books and Help files that came with the MINITAB software, assumes that you know the basics of using your computer—how to start applications, use your mouse, move and close windows, etc. If you need help doing these tasks, consult your system documentation.

What you will learn

MINITAB *Essentials* introduces you to the MINITAB environment and provides a quick overview of some of the most important features. For a step-by-step tutorial of some of this same information, see Chapter 8, *Session One: MINITAB Basics*.

If your screen looks different

MINITAB for Windows Release 13 can be used with Windows 95, Windows 98, and Windows NT 4.0. Depending on which version of Windows you are using, the pictures of dialog boxes, windows, and other software features you see in the documentation may not exactly match what you see on your screen.

Don't worry—the *contents* of the dialog boxes and windows, as well as the steps you follow to do something in MINITAB, are almost always the same no matter what version of Windows you use. Where there are exceptions, the documentation will point them out.

Starting and Exiting

▶ **To start MINITAB**

1 From the Taskbar, choose **Start ➤ Programs ➤ Minitab 13 for Windows ➤ Minitab**.

▶ **To exit MINITAB**

1 Choose **File ➤ Exit**.

The MINITAB Environment

As you perform your data analysis, you will work with many different MINITAB windows and tools. Here is a brief overview of the parts of the MINITAB environment:

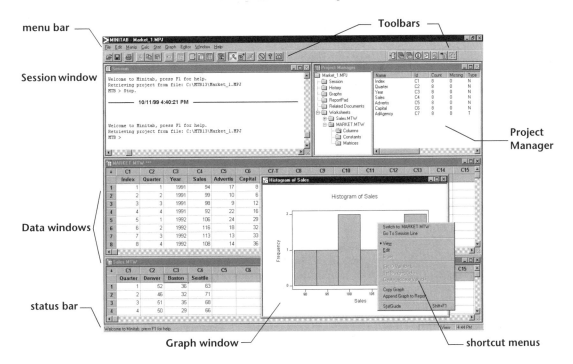

MINITAB windows

- The **Session window** displays text output such as tables of statistics.

- **Data windows** are where you enter, edit, and view the column data for each worksheet.

- **Graph windows** display graphs. You can have up to 100 Graph windows open at a time.

Project Manager

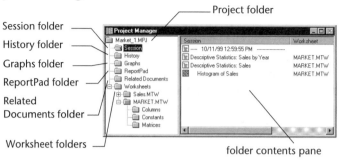

- Session folder
- History folder
- Graphs folder
- ReportPad folder
- Related Documents folder
- Worksheet folders
- Project folder
- folder contents pane

The Project Manager contains folders that allow you to navigate, view, and manipulate various parts of your project. By right-clicking on either the folders or the folder contents, you can access a variety of menus that allow you to manage Session window output, graphs, worksheets, command language, and related project areas.

The...	Contains...	Use this folder to...
Session folder	a list of ■ all Session window output by command ■ all graphs	manage Session window output. For instance: ■ jump to Session window output ■ copy, delete, rename, or print Session window output or graphs ■ append Session window output or graphs to the ReportPad
History folder	all the commands you have used	■ repeat complex command sequences ■ use commands to create macros
Graph folder	a list of all graphs	manage your graphs. For instance: ■ arrange, rename, tile, or remove your graphs ■ append graphs to the ReportPad
ReportPad folder	the ReportPad basic word processing tool	■ create, arrange, or edit reports of project work ■ move ReportPad contents to a more powerful word processing program for further editing and layout
Related Documents folder	a list of program files, documents, or internet URLs that are related to your MINITAB project	quickly access project-related, non-MINITAB files for easy reference

The...	Contains...	Use this folder to...
Worksheet folder	the **Columns**, **Constants**, **Matrices**, and **Design** folders for each open worksheet	View summaries of worksheet information, including: ■ column counts, missing values, column descriptions ■ constants ■ matrices ■ design summary

Menus and tools

- The **menu bar** is where you choose commands. See *Menu commands* on page 1-7.

- The **Standard Toolbar** displays buttons for commonly used functions—the buttons change depending on which MINITAB window is active. See *Toolbars* on page 1-7.

- The **Project Manager Toolbar** provides shortcuts to Project Manager folders.

- The **status bar** displays explanatory text whenever you are pointing to a menu item or Toolbar button.

- **Shortcut menus** appear when you right-click on any window in MINITAB or on any folder in the Project Manager. The menu displays the most commonly-used functions for that window or folder.

- Two graph editing palettes (not shown), the **Tool palette** and the **Attribute palette**, let you add and change elements on graphs. See *Graph Editing* on page 5-8.

Work Flow in MINITAB

There are many steps you may take in a typical analysis. Each of the six chapters that follow this one correspond to a basic step in your analysis. Each chapter provides an overview of that step, and shows you how to perform some of the most common tasks for that part of your analysis.

The basic tasks and procedures that can be used throughout all the steps—such as issuing commands and working with projects—are described later in this chapter.

Here is a list of the chapters and a brief description of some of the tasks you will learn:

Chapter and title	Shows you how to...
2 *Managing Data*	enter and edit data in a Data window, add data from files and save to files, and generate patterned data
3 *Manipulating and Calculating Data*	manipulate columns of data in the Data window, sort and subset data, and create equations
4 *Using Data Analysis and Quality Tools*	use a variety of analysis procedures, from basic statistics to quality control
5 *Graphing Data*	create, edit, and brush graphs, as well as print and save graphs in a variety of formats
6 *Managing the Session Window and Generating Reports*	navigate through text output and change the format of text, as well as print and save output in a variety of formats
7 *Session Commands and Macros*	use command language interactively or within a macro. Macros are useful for automating repetitive tasks.

Issuing Commands

In MINITAB, there are three ways to access commands: with menus, the Toolbar, and session commands.

Most commands use data in some way: they draw graphs based on the data, change existing data, or create data. Data are stored in worksheets, and a project can contain many worksheets. When you issue a command (by any method) that uses data, the command acts on the *current worksheet*. The current worksheet is the one associated with the *active Data window*. You make a window active by clicking on it, by choosing it from the Window menu, or by right-clicking on its corresponding folder in the Project Manager, and selecting **Bring to Front**. If no Data window is active, the command acts on the Data window that was most recently active.

Tip | You can tell which Data window contains the current (or active) worksheet by looking at the window's title bar. The current worksheet will have three asterisks in the title, like this:

Menu commands

- **Menu bar**: Click on an item in the menu bar to open the menu, then click on a menu item to execute the command, open a submenu, or open a dialog box.

- **Shortcut menu**: Right-click in a MINITAB window to open the shortcut menu, then click on a menu item as in regular menus.

If a menu item is dimmed, it is currently unavailable.

Tip | To recall the last dialog box you used in your current MINITAB session, choose **Edit ➤ Edit Last Dialog** or press Ctrl+E.

When you open most dialog boxes, MINITAB "remembers" all of its settings from the last time you used the dialog box in this session, or in a saved project. To clear a dialog box of all of its settings and return it to the default state, press F3.

Toolbars

MINITAB's toolbars are a quick way to issue commands. When you click a toolbar button, MINITAB performs an action or opens a dialog box, exactly like the corresponding menu command.

MINITAB's toolbars are detachable. You can click on them and drag them anywhere within the MINITAB environment for easy access. Detached toolbars always remain on top of any windows.

The Standard Toolbar

The Standard Toolbar buttons change depending on which MINITAB window is active. For example, here is the Standard Toolbar when the Data window is active.

The Data window Standard Toolbar

Tip | To see the name of the button, place your mouse pointer over the button.
To hide the Toolbar, choose **Window ➤ Hide Toolbar**.

More | When you edit graphs, two floating graph palettes also display. For details, see Chapter 5, *Graphing Data*.

The Project Manager Toolbar

The Project Manager Toolbar buttons remain the same no matter which window is active. Project Manager Toolbar buttons give you shortcuts to the Project Manager folders.

When you click on one of the Project Manager Toolbar buttons, the Project Manager window is maximized with the appropriate folder displayed, or the folder contents are displayed and tiled with a corresponding worksheet. To return to your previous window arrangement, press the appropriate Project Manager Toolbar button again.

The Project Manager Toolbar

Entering variables in a dialog box

MINITAB's dialog boxes are like most of the ones you have used in other software. One feature that may be new to you is MINITAB's variable list box, which appears in many dialog boxes. The variable list box displays columns, stored constants, or matrices and lets you enter them into any text box that can accept variables. Of course, you can always type the variable name in the text box, but using the variables list box is usually faster and more error-free.

The variable list box contains columns, constants, and matrices from the current worksheet.

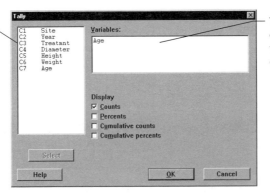

The **Variables** text box can accept only columns. When the cursor is in this box, the variable list box (left) displays only columns.

When you click on or place your cursor in a text box that can accept a variable, the variable list box displays all the variables in the current worksheet that are valid choices. For example, if the text box can accept only columns (but not matrices or stored constants), the variable list box will display only columns. If the text box can accept only numeric columns (but not text or date/time columns), the variable list box will display only numeric columns.

Note | If the variable list box doesn't display the variables you expected, make sure that the worksheet you want is current: click **Cancel** to leave the dialog box, click on the Data window that belongs to the worksheet you want, then press Ctrl+E to return to the dialog box.

▶ **To select multiple variables with the mouse**

1 Click in the text box you want to fill.

2 Click in the variable list box.

3 Click on individual variables, drag across several variables, or hold down Ctrl and click on discontiguous variables.

4 Click **Select**.

▶ **To select a single variable with the mouse (quick method)**

1 Click in the text box you want to fill.

2 Move your mouse pointer to the variable list box and double-click on the variable you want.

▶ **To select a variable using the keyboard**

1 Tab to the text box you want to fill.

2 Press F2. This makes the variable list box active.

3 Using the up- and down-arrow keys, move to variable you want.

4 Press F2. This selects the variable and makes the text box active again.

Session commands

Session commands are a useful alternative to menu commands, especially when making macros to automate repetitive analyses. Most session commands are simple, easy to remember words, like PLOT, SAVE, or SORT. You can type commands in two places: the Command Line Editor and the Session window. Most often you will find it easier to use the Command Line Editor.

▶ **To use the Command Line Editor**

1 Choose **Edit ➤ Command Line Editor**.

Paste, type, and edit commands here. ────

Use the scroll bars to see more commands.

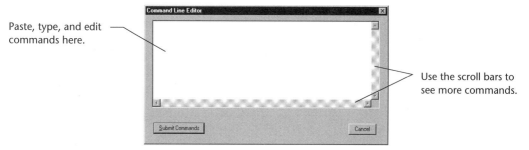

2 Do one of the following:

  ■ Type the session commands—see *Basic Rules for Typing Session Commands* on page 7-3.

  ■ Paste them from the History folder by pressing [Ctrl]+[V].

3 Click **Submit Commands**.

Working with Projects

A MINITAB project contains all your work: the data, text output from commands, graphs, and more. When you save the project, you save all of your work at once. When you open a project, you can pick up right where you left off. You can have only one project open at a time.

The project's many pieces can be handled individually. You can create data, graphs, and output from within MINITAB. You can also add data and graphs to the project by copying them from files. The contents of most windows can be saved and printed separately from the project, in a variety of file formats. You can also *discard* a worksheet or graph, which removes the item from the project without saving it. See *Working with Individual Windows* on page 1-12.

Opening, saving, and closing projects

When you save the project, you save all the information about your work:

  ■ the contents of all the windows, including
    – the columns of data in each Data window
    – each Graph window
    – the complete text in the Session window and the History folder
    – the stored constants, matrices, and design objects (used with the design of experiments commands) that are summarized in the Worksheets folder

        – the contents of the ReportPad folder

        – any file links stored in the Related Documents folder

- the description of the project created with **File ➤ Project Description**

- the description of each worksheet created with **Editor ➤ Worksheet Description**

- the size, location, and state of each window

- the contents of each dialog box you used

▶ To open, save, or close a project

- To open a new project, choose **File ➤ New**, click **Project**, and click **OK**.

- To open a saved project, choose **File ➤ Open Project**.

- To save a project, choose **File ➤ Save Project**.

- To close a project, you must open a new project, open a saved project, or exit MINITAB.

Tip | You can perform any of the above actions by right-clicking on the Project (or Untitled) folder in the Project Manager.

Note | If you close a project before saving it, MINITAB will prompt you to save the project. You choose to save the entire project in a project file, or save pieces of the project in separate files. For details on separate files, see *Saving the contents of each window* on page 1-14.

Saving project preferences

When you save a project, you not only save the contents of windows and dialog boxes, you also save their size, location, and appearance. If you want to use these same settings when you start a new project, you can save your preferences.

▶ To save your preferences

1 Choose **Edit ➤ Preferences**.

2 Click the category of preferences you want to save, such as **Data window** or **DDE links**, then click **Select**.

3 Change the settings you want, click **OK**, then click **Save**.
The next time you start a new project, MINITAB will use these settings.

Working with Individual Windows

Projects are made up of data, text output, graphs, and information about the current working environment. Most of this information is visible in one of MINITAB's windows; for example, the text output is visible in the Session window. Data in MINITAB is slightly unusual in that the contents are visible in more than one window—see *Understanding data and worksheets* on page 1-12.

Much of the content of various windows is created within MINITAB. For example, the Session window contains the output of analysis commands, the Project Manager History folder holds all the commands you have used, and the Data window can contain data that you have typed in directly.

Worksheet data and graphs, however, can also come from outside files—see *Adding worksheets and graphs from files* on page 1-12. Worksheets and graphs can also be *discarded*, that is removed, from the project—see *Closing worksheets and graphs* on page 1-13. The Session window cannot be discarded.

The contents of all of the windows can be saved into a separate file and printed.

Note | The number of Data windows you can have open at one time is limited only by your computer's memory.
| You can have up to 100 Graph windows open at one time.

Understanding data and worksheets

Each data set you work with in a project is contained in a *worksheet*. You can have many worksheets in one project—the number of worksheets is limited only by your computer's memory.

View and edit a worksheet's contents through MINITAB windows and commands:

- View your data in MINITAB's Data and Session windows, and in the Project Manager Worksheet folder

- Edit columns of data in a Data window (one Data window for each worksheet)

- Manipulate and analyze data using commands

When you issue a command that effects your data, the command acts on the current worksheet. For details, see *Issuing Commands* on page 1-6.

Adding worksheets and graphs from files

You can add worksheets and graphs to the project by copying from data and graph files. Worksheet data can be from MINITAB worksheet (MTW) files, or from other applications, like Excel. Graph window content can come only from MINITAB Graphics Format (MGF) files.

Worksheet and graph files work differently than in earlier releases of MINITAB. When you open a file, you are *copying* the contents of the file to the project. That means that any changes you make to the worksheet or graph inside the project will not affect the file itself. If you do want the changes to be reflected in that file, you can save the worksheet or graph with that same name, overwriting the old file's contents.

▶ To add worksheet data or graphs from a file

1 Choose **File ➤ Open Worksheet** or **File ➤ Open Graph**.

   This opens a standard Windows file dialog box. For help on using the dialog box, click the **Help** button.

2 Select a directory and file name.

   If you are opening a worksheet, by default the dialog box displays the file names of all MINITAB worksheet (MTW) files. If you want to copy data from a file that is not a worksheet (for example, a MINITAB project (MPJ) file or an Excel file), select that file type from the **Files of type** drop-down list.

3 Click **Open**.

   A message box will appear, telling you that a copy of the content of this file will be added to the worksheet. If you do not want this message to appear every time you open a file, check **Do not display this message again**.

4 Click **OK**.

More | For more information on opening worksheet files, see *Opening, Saving, and Printing Files* on page 2-10.

Closing worksheets and graphs

When you no longer need the worksheet or graph in your project, you can close it. Closing removes the item from the project, and the data or graphs are gone forever.

You can close a worksheet or graph by clicking the close button on the Data or Graph window's title bar (just as you would close any window on your system), or you can use the menus as described below.

▶ To close a worksheet

1 Make the desired Data window active.

2 Choose **File ➤ Close Worksheet**.

3 MINITAB will ask if you want to save the worksheet first. Click **Yes**, **No**, or **Cancel**, as you prefer.

Tip | You can also perform the above action by right-clicking on the Project Manager Worksheet folder and selecting **Close**.

▶ **To close graphs**

1 Left-click on the Graphs folder in the Project Manager.

2 Click on or drag to select one or more graphs

3 Press ⌈Delete⌋ or right-click on the selected graphs and choose **Delete**.

More | You can close all graphs at once by choosing **Window ➤ Close All Graphs** or clicking
the 🖼 button on the Toolbar.

Saving the contents of each window

You can also individually save and print the contents of any window. This is handy if
you want to share one particular data set with a colleague, export a certain graph so it
can be used in another MINITAB session, or use the Session window text in a word
processor.

▶ **To save the contents of a window**

1 Activate the window you want to save.

2 Choose **File ➤ Save [window type] As**.

3 Pick a file type—see the table below.

4 Enter a file name and click **OK**.

Available file types

You can save your data and results in various file types, depending on what you want to
save.

Save these contents	as these file types	File extension
Session window output	■ Plain text—no fonts ■ Rich Text Format—fonts ■ List files—same as plain text	■ TXT ■ RTF ■ LIS
Worksheet data that will work in MINITAB Release 13: columns, constants, matrices, and all other worksheet features	■ MINITAB 13 worksheet	■ MTW
Worksheet data that will work in an earlier release of MINITAB: columns, constants, matrices, and worksheet features specific to that release	■ MINITAB 12 worksheet ■ MINITAB 11 worksheet ■ MINITAB 10 worksheet	■ MTW

Save these contents	as these file types	File extension
Worksheet data that will work in any release of MINITAB: columns, constants, and matrices	■ Portable worksheet	■ MTP
Columns only	■ Excel ■ Lotus 1-2-3 ■ and more	■ XLS ■ WK1
Graphs	■ MINITAB Graphics Format (graphs that can be re-opened in MINITAB)	■ MGF
	■ Graphics formats that can be used in other applications, such as bitmap format	■ BMP ■ TIF ■ JPG ■ PNG
History folder contents	■ Plain text with a variety of file extensions; for example, MAC files are MINITAB macros.	■ TXT ■ MAC ■ and more
ReportPad folder contents	■ Rich text format (stores fonts and OLE embedded graphics)	■ RTF

Printing the contents of windows

▶ To print a window

1 Make the window active.

2 Choose **File ➤ Print** [window name].

3 If you are printing a Data window, MINITAB will display an options dialog box. Select the options you want, and click **OK**.

4 In the Print dialog box, click **OK**.

Tip | To print a portion of the window, first select the text or cells you want, follow steps 1–3 as above, then in the Print dialog box make sure **Print Range** is set to **Selection**.

Getting Answers and Information

This book is designed to give you an overview of the most important features of MINITAB, but sooner or later you will want more details. You have several resources for finding answers.

Resource	Description	How to get it
ReadMe file	Late-breaking information on this release of MINITAB, including details on changes to the software or documentation	From the Windows taskbar, choose **Start ➤ Programs ➤ Minitab 13 for Windows ➤ ReadMe file**.
Online Help	Complete documentation on each MINITAB feature and concept, written for users of menus and dialog boxes, and organized especially for online viewing	In MINITAB, you can ■ choose **Help ➤ Search Help** ■ click the **Help** button in any dialog box ■ press F1 at any time ■ click ⚷ on the Toolbar
Session Command Help	Documentation on each session command, including syntax and examples	From the Start menu, choose **Programs ➤ Minitab 13 for Windows ➤ Session Command Help** or **Help ➤ Session Command Help**.
StatGuide	Provides statistical guidance after you run a procedure in MINITAB, primarily focusing on the interpretation of results.	■ click ⊞ on the Toolbar ■ press Shift+F1 ■ right-click in the active window or on a Session title in the Project Manager Session folder, and choose **StatGuide** ■ choose **Help ➤ StatGuide**
What's New	If you are upgrading to Release 13 from a previous release of MINITAB, check out the *What's New* Help file.	From the Start menu, choose **Programs ➤ Minitab 13 for Windows ➤ What's New**.
Feature List	If this is your first release of MINITAB, check out the *Feature List* Help file.	From the Start menu, choose **Programs ➤ Minitab 13 for Windows ➤ Feature List**.
User's Guides	Two printed books give you the details on using MINITAB, from opening files to performing complex analyses: ■ *User's Guide 1: Data, Graphics, and Macros* ■ *User's Guide 2: Data Analysis and Quality Tools*	If you did not receive the user's guides with your copy of the software, you may have purchased MINITAB under a special licensing agreement. To order, contact Minitab Inc. See *How to Contact MINITAB* in the installation guide that came with your software.

Resource	Description	How to get it
User's Guides and Meet MINITAB online	All of the printed documentation is available online as PDF files. The Adobe Acrobat Reader is provided for your convenience.	Perform a Custom install to setup access to the online books. During the installation process you can choose to install the online books on your hard disk drive, or use them directly from the CD. To access the online books, from the Start menu, choose **Programs ➤ Minitab 13 for Windows ➤** *book name*.
Customer support	Highly-skilled customer support specialists are ready to help you.	See *How to Contact MINITAB* in the installation guide that came with your software.
Internet	At Minitab's web site you can get answers to common technical questions, download macros, and download free maintenance releases of MINITAB.	Go to *HTTP://www.minitab.com* and follow the support links.

Where to Go Next

Now that you have an idea of how to use MINITAB to analyze your data, what is the best way to proceed?

If you would like more practice with MINITAB, turn to the *Sample Sessions* which begin with Chapter 8, *Session One: MINITAB Basics*. These are step-by-step tutorials that guide you through sample analyses.

Or just jump in and begin your own analysis, referring to online Help or the printed documentation whenever you have a question.

2
Managing Data

Managing Data Overview

In this chapter, you will see the many ways for you to bring data into MINITAB. You can type data, copy and paste it, or generate it from within MINITAB, and of course, open it from files.

When you are finished working with the data, you can save it to use later in MINITAB or another application. Or you can print a hard copy.

But first, you should become familiar with some of the terminology and concepts used when managing your data in MINITAB.

Data are contained in worksheets

In MINITAB, all the data associated with a particular data set are contained in a *worksheet*. A project can have many worksheets—the number of worksheets is limited only by your computer's memory.

A worksheet can contain three types of data—numeric, text, and date/time—in three forms: columns, constants, or matrices. You can view your data in several windows, but most of the time you will work with columns of data in the Data window.

Three types of data: numeric, text, and date/time

- *Numeric* data are numbers.

- *Text* data are characters that can consist of a mix of letters, numbers, spaces, and special characters, such as "Test Number 4" or "North Carolina."

- *Date/time* data can be dates (such as Jan-1-1997 or 3/17/97), times (such as 08:25:22 AM), or both (such as 3/17/97 08:25:22 AM). MINITAB internally stores dates and times as numbers, but displays them in whatever format you choose.

Data can take three forms: column, stored constant, or matrix

Form	Contains...	Referred to by Number	Name	Number available
Column	numeric, text, or date/time data	C + a number, as in C1 or C22	'Sales' or 'Year'	Limited only by system memory, up to a maximum of 4000
Stored Constant	a single number or a text string (e.g., "New York")	K + a number, as in K1or K93	'First' or 'Counter'	1000
Matrix	a rectangular block of cells containing numbers	M + a number, as in M1 or M44	'Inverse'	100

Columns, constants, and matrices are all:

- affected by menu and session commands

- named with the session command NAME (documented in Help)—though columns can also be named in the Data window

- saved to a file when you choose **File ➤ Save Current Worksheet (As)** or **File ➤ Save Project (As)**

- summarized in the Project Manager Worksheets folder

Three windows to work with data

The Data window

This window contains the columns of data that are in the worksheet. When you have multiple worksheets open, each worksheet has its own Data window.

column number   column name   The -T says this is a   The -D says this is a
                                              text column.   date/time column.
row number

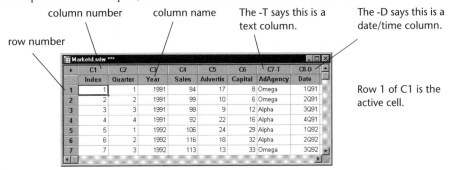

Row 1 of C1 is the active cell.

In each Data window you can

- view the columns of data that are in the worksheet

- enter values and edit them in various ways (see the following pages)

- manipulate columns in various ways, including changing the format, font, name, width, description, and position of columns (described in Chapter 3, *Manipulating and Calculating Data*)

Note | Data windows are not spreadsheets.

Although the Data window has rows and columns, it is not a spreadsheet like Microsoft Excel or Lotus 1-2-3. In MINITAB, cells contain values that you type or generate with commands. Cells do not contain formulas that update based on other cells.

For example, if you want column C3 to equal the values in C1 plus the values in C2, you would use the Calculator to generate the values for C3 (see *Using the Calculator* on page 3-14). If you change the values in C1, C3 does not change until you use the Calculator again or use some other command to change C3's contents.

The Worksheet folder

The Worksheet folder in the Project Manager summarizes the columns, stored constants, matrices, and design objects used in the current worksheet. You can look at information for other worksheets in your project by clicking on their Worksheet folders. This summary is especially handy as a reference when you are trying to spot unequal column lengths or columns that contain missing values. The Worksheet folder content window is updated automatically.

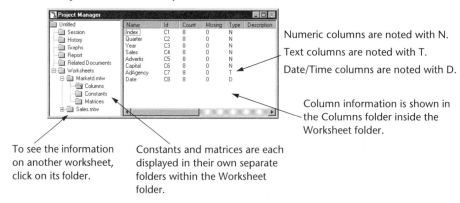

Numeric columns are noted with N.

Text columns are noted with T.

Date/Time columns are noted with D.

Column information is shown in the Columns folder inside the Worksheet folder.

To see the information on another worksheet, click on its folder.

Constants and matrices are each displayed in their own separate folders within the Worksheet folder.

The Session window

You can display columns, constants, and matrices in this window when you choose
Manip ➤ Display Data.

"Mean Sales" is a constant.

"Sales by Year" is a matrix.

"Sales" is a column.

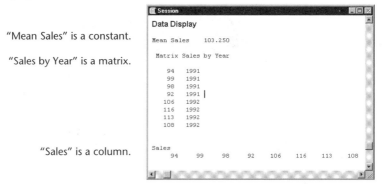

Typing Data into the Data Window

To enter a value in a Data window cell, just click on the cell, type a value, and press
(Enter). You can enter multiple values in any order you wish: column by column, row by
row, or in blocks

Each column generally represents a variable.

Each row generally
represents an
individual case, or
observation.

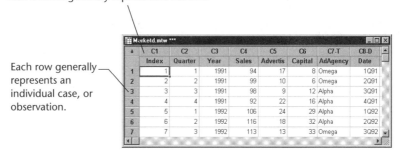

Entering data automatically formats the column. When you type an entry into an
empty column, MINITAB assigns a data type to the column: numeric, text, or date/time.
If the data type is not numeric, MINITAB also adds an identifier next to the column
number: D for date/time data and T for text data.

More   You can change data from one type to another. See *Changing column data types* on page
3-7.

▶ **To open a new (empty) Data window**

1 Choose **File ➤ New**.

2 Select **Minitab Worksheet** and click **OK**.

Entering data in columns, rows, or blocks

▶ **To enter data columnwise**

1 Click the data direction arrow to make it point down.

2 Enter your data, pressing `Tab` or `Enter` to move the active cell. Press `Ctrl`+`Enter` to move the active cell to the top of the next column.

data direction arrow

For example, click in row 1, column 1, then type:
   Owen `Enter`
   Logan `Enter`
   Baker `Enter`
Notice that after you type a value and press `Enter`, the active cell moves down.

▶ **To enter data rowwise**

1 Click the data direction arrow to make it point to the right.

2 Enter your data. Press `Ctrl`+`Enter` to move the active cell to the beginning of the next row.

data direction arrow

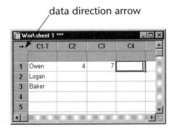

For example, click in row 1, column 2, then type:
   4 `Enter` *7* `Enter`

Notice that after you type a value and press `Enter`, the active cell moves right.

▶ **To enter data within a block**

1 Highlight the area you want to work in.

2 Enter your data. The active cell moves only within the selected area.

3 To unselect the area, press an arrow key or click anywhere in the Data window.

For example:

- With the mouse, point to the cell at row 2, column 2.
- Drag down and to the right. This selects the block.
- Type:
  5 [Enter] 8 [Enter]
  6 [Enter] 9 [Enter]

Notice that if you select a block before typing values, pressing [Enter] moves the active cell to the next cell in the block. Pressing any arrow key unhighlights the block.

If you make a mistake

▶ To correct a value in a cell

- To delete the old value and enter a new one, click the cell, type the correct value, and press [Enter].

- To change a portion of the cell contents, double-click the cell, then use the arrow, [Backspace] and [Del] keys to make the changes.

▶ To undo a change

- If you have just typed a new value in a cell, and have not yet pressed [Enter], press [Esc] to restore the previous value of the cell.

Copying and Pasting Data

Copying and pasting is a quick way to enter data that is in another application or in another MINITAB window. You can copy from:

- cells in the same Data window, or from cells in another Data window

- another spreadsheet package, such as Lotus 1-2-3 or Microsoft Excel

- a table in a word processor or text in the body of a word processing document

- the MINITAB Session window

▶ To copy from anywhere and paste into the Data window

1 Highlight the data you want and copy it. In MINITAB, the copy command is **Edit ➤ Copy**.

2 In one of MINITAB's Data windows, select one or more cells, then choose **Edit ➤ Paste Cells**.

3   If you selected more than one cell, MINITAB will replace the contents of those cells with the contents from the Clipboard.

If you selected one cell, MINITAB will ask how you want to paste data. Do one of the following and click **OK**:

■   Choose **Insert above the active cell, shifting cells down to make room**.

■   Choose **Replace the active cell**.

4   One of the following happens, depending on whether the data on the Clipboard is separated (or delimited) by tabs or spaces. Data copied from MINITAB's Data window, most spreadsheet packages, and word processor tables are tab-delimited. Data copied from MINITAB's Session window and the body of word processing documents are space-delimited.

■   If the data are separated by tabs, MINITAB automatically puts each value into its own cell.

■   If the data are separated by spaces, MINITAB displays a dialog box that shows the first line of data and asks how MINITAB should interpret the spaces. Do one of the following:
    –   If the line of data looks right, click **Use spaces as delimiters**.
    –   If you would prefer to paste all the data into one column, click **Paste as a single column**.

Note | If you paste entire columns of data, and any have column names that already exist in the current worksheet, MINITAB will automatically add a numbered suffix to the name of each duplicate column to be added. For example, YOURDATA will become YOURDATA_0.

Tip | To undo the whole pasting procedure, choose **Edit ➤ Undo Paste**.

Generating Patterned Data

You can generate data that follow a pattern. You can generate a simple set of numbers that follows a sequence, or a list of numbers that have an arbitrary order. You can also generate patterned date/time data.

The most common task is to fill a column with a simple set of numbers that follow a sequence: for example, all the numbers from 1 to 100, or all the even numbers between 1 to 50. Optionally, each value in the list can be repeated, or the entire sequence can be repeated. Repeating values or entire sequences can be very useful for entering factor levels for analysis of variance designs.

More | You can also generate random data—see Help for details.

To generate patterned data in Minitab, use either the **Autofill** feature or the **Make Patterned Data** command. **Autofill** allows you to manually fill data window cells with patterned data by clicking and dragging with the mouse. **Make Patterned Data** allows you to create patterned data using a dialog box.

Note | Because data in MINITAB are column oriented, you can use Autofill to fill one or more columns with patterned data (dragging up or down), but you cannot create patterned data across rows (dragging horizontally).

▶ To Autofill cells

1   Highlight one or more cells in one or more columns.

2   Place the mouse cursor over the Autofill handle in the lower-right corner of the highlighted cells. When the mouse is over the handle, a cross symbol (+) will appear.

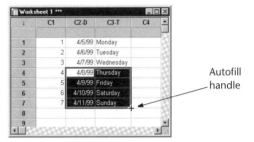

For some tasks, you can hold Ctrl down to change the way Autofill operates. When you hold Ctrl down, a superscript cross will appear above the Autofill cross symbol ($+^+$). For details on Autofill functionality, see Chapter 5, *Generating Patterned Data* in *User's Guide 1: Data, Graphics, and Macros*.

3   Left click and drag outside the highlighted cells to create patterned data, and inside the selection to delete cells (if more than one cell is highlighted).

Note | When Autofill is activated, MINITAB's status bar provides feedback on Autofill's current operation.

▶ To generate a simple set of numbers

1   Choose **Calc ➤ Make Patterned Data ➤ Simple Set of Numbers**.

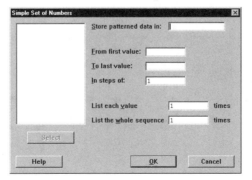

2   In the text box for **Store patterned data in**, enter the name or number of a new or existing column where you want the patterned data to go.

3 Enter numbers in the **From first value**, **To last value**, and **In steps of** text boxes.

4 Optionally, enter a number in **List each value** and/or **List the whole sequence**.

▷ **Examples of patterned data expressions**

To get...	From first value	To last value	In steps of	List each value	List the whole sequence
all the numbers from 1 to 100	1	100	1	1	1
all even numbers from 10 to 1: 10 8 6 4 2	10	1	2	1	1
every tenth between -0.5 and -0.1: -0.5 -0.4 -0.3 -0.2 -0.1	-0.5	-0.1	0.1	1	1
five 1's, five 2's, five 3's, and five 4's: 11111222223333344444	1	4	1	5	1
two sets of the sequence 12345, repeating each number: 11223344551122334455	1	5	1	2	2

Opening, Saving, and Printing Files

You can add data to your project by copying it from a file. The contents of each file are stored in a worksheet.

When you open a project file, all the worksheets that were inside that project when you last saved are available to you. When you save a project, the data are saved with that project.

Most of the time, the data files you will bring into your project will be MINITAB worksheets. Those worksheets may be stand-alone files (files with the extension MTW), or parts of a project (MPJ) file. You can preview a project file to see a list of all the worksheets in the file, then copy one of the worksheets from that project to your own.

You can also open and save data files from many other applications like Excel and Lotus 1-2-3, or exchange data with versions of MINITAB on other platforms using MINITAB portable worksheets (MTP files). You can also import data from other applications using tools like Open Database Connectivity (ODBC) and Dynamic Data Exchange (DDE).

Opening data files

▶ To open data from a file

1   Choose **File ➤ Open Worksheet**.

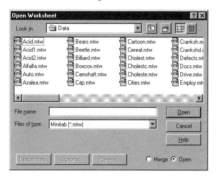

The appearance of this dialog box may be different on your computer, depending on which operating system you are using. For details, see your system documentation.

2   In the **Files of type** box, choose the type of file you are looking for: Excel, Lotus 1-2-3, MINITAB portable worksheet, etc.

3   Select a file.

4   If you like, use any of the options below, then click **Open**.

Options

- When you select a MINITAB worksheet file, click **Description** to read the worksheet description, or click **Preview** to see the data before you open it. When you are *merging* a MINITAB file (see below), the Preview dialog box also lets you select which columns you want to merge and where to place them.

- When you select a MINITAB project file, click **Preview** to see which worksheets are contained in the file. In that Preview dialog box, you can also view descriptions for each worksheet.

- When you select a non-MINITAB file, click **Preview** to see how MINITAB will interpret the rows and columns. If you like, change column settings in the Preview dialog box, or click **Options** to change other settings.

- For any file type, you can choose to **Open** or **Merge** the file. Opening creates a new worksheet that contains the data. Merging adds the data to the current worksheet.

Saving data

▶ **To save data as part of the project**

1 Choose **File** ➤ **Save Project**.

▶ **To save data into a separate file**

1 Make the desired Data window active.

2 Choose **File** ➤ **Save Current Worksheet As**.

3 In **Files of type**, choose the data format in which you want the data to be saved.

4 Select a directory, enter a file name, and click **OK**.

Printing data

▶ **To print the contents of the Data window**

1 Make the desired Data window active.

2 Choose **File** ➤ **Print Worksheet**.

3 Select or unselect options (at right), then click **OK**.

4 The standard Windows Print dialog box will appear. If you need instructions for using this dialog box, click the dialog box's **Help** button.

▶ **To print all data, including matrices and constants**

1 Choose **Manip** ➤ **Display Data**.

2 In the text box for **Columns, constants, and matrices to display**, enter the variables and click **OK**. The data will appear in the Session window.

3 In the Session window, select the text.

4 Choose **File** ➤ **Print Session Window**.

5 Make sure **Print Range** is set to **Selection**, and click **OK**.

Working with Database and Special Text Files

This chapter has touched on only the most common ways to get your data into MINITAB. You can also get data from other applications in three other ways:

- If the other application is a Windows program, you can use Dynamic Data Exchange (DDE) to bring the data into MINITAB. Use the **Edit ➤ Links** command to create a link between the other application and MINITAB. DDE has several other uses besides collecting data, and the complete set of DDE features is described in Help.

- If the other application is a database, you can use Open Database Connectivity (ODBC) to import the data. ODBC is a protocol used by many database applications that allows you to query the database and import data. In MINITAB, use the **File ➤ Query Database (ODBC)** command. For details and instructions, see Help.

- If all else fails, you can use MINITAB's ability to read text files in a format that you specify. Most data-using applications on most platforms can generate a text file. If MINITAB does not correctly interpret rows and columns when you use the **File ➤ Open Worksheet** command, you can use **File ➤ Other Files ➤ Import Special Text** to specify a custom format. For instructions, see Help.

3

Manipulating and Calculating Data

Manipulating and Calculating Data Overview

Once you have data in a MINITAB project, you may need to rearrange or reorganize the data before you begin your analyses. You can move or delete rows and columns, convert data from one type to another (such as changing numeric data to date/time data), or control the way data is displayed in Data windows and graphs (such as displaying a date as 1/1/97 or January 1, 1997).

You can also create new variables that are based on the original variables. You can combine columns, create subsets of columns, or fill a column with values that are calculated from values in other columns.

Manipulating Cells, Rows, and Columns

You can perform a variety of actions on cells, rows, and columns in the Data window.

Before performing an action, you often select the area you want to affect. If you do not select a row or column before doing an operation that affects the entire row or column (such as insert column), the column that contains the active cell is considered selected.

Selecting areas of the Data window

▶ **To select...**	**Do this**
a block of cells	drag across the cells
one or more entire rows	drag across the row numbers
one or more entire columns	drag across the column numbers
all the cells	choose **Edit ➤ Select All Cells**

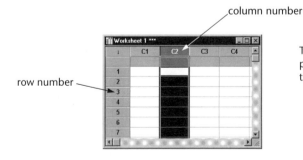

column number

row number

The active cell is always part of the selection—in this case, row 1 of C2.

Finding specific data in the Data window

▶ To find words, numbers, or dates in the Data window

1 With the Data window active, choose **Editor ➤ Find**.

2 In **Find what**, type the characters you want to search for.

3 Click **Find Next**.

More | MINITAB also has a feature for automatically replacing text, numbers, or dates in the Data window—see *To find and replace text, numbers, or date/time strings* on page 3-6.

Cutting, clearing, and deleting

Before cutting, clearing, or deleting, select an area or click on the cell you want to make active.

▶ To delete...

To delete...	Do this
cells and put them on the Clipboard (following rows or columns move up or left)	Choose **Edit ➤ Cut Cells**.
cell contents only (empty cells remain)	Choose **Edit ➤ Clear Cells**, or press [Backspace]. In a numeric column, MINITAB inserts * in a cleared cell (unless it is the last cell in a column).
cells (following rows or columns move up or left)	Choose **Edit ➤ Delete Cells** or press [Delete].

Copying and pasting

Before copying or pasting, select an area or click on the cell you want to make active.

▶ **To copy...**   **Do this**

cells to the Clipboard	Choose **Edit ➤ Copy Cells**.
certain rows of columns This command copies columns from one part of a Data window to another part of a Data window, using or omitting rows you specify.	1 Choose **Manip ➤ Copy Columns**. 2 Click **Use rows** or **Omit rows**. 3 Enter criteria and click **OK**.

▶ **To paste cells from the Clipboard and...**   **Do this**

replace other cells	1 Select any number of cells. 2 Choose **Edit ➤ Paste Cells**. Note: if you select a greater number of cells than were copied to the Clipboard, MINITAB will fill the additional cells by pasting repeating blocks of the copied data.
insert above a cell	1 Click on a cell. 2 Choose **Edit ➤ Paste Cells**. 3 A dialog box apears. Choose **Insert above the active cell** and click **OK**.

Note | If you paste from another MINITAB window, such as the Session window, or from another application, MINITAB may prompt you for instructions on how to paste the data. See *Copying and Pasting Data* on page 2-7.

Inserting emtpy cells, rows, and columns

▶ **To insert cells, rows, or columns**

1 Select one or more cells.

2 Choose **Editor ➤ Insert Cells/Insert Rows/Insert Columns**.

Cells and rows are inserted above the selection, columns are inserted to the left of the selection.

MINITAB inserts the same number of items that are selected. For example, if cells in three rows are selected when you choose **Editor ➤ Insert Rows**, three rows are inserted.

Moving columns

▶ To move columns

1 Select one or more columns.

2 Choose **Editor ➤ Move Columns**.

3 Select one of the following and click **OK**.

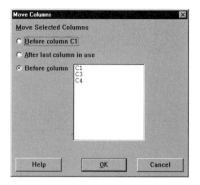

- **Before column C1** inserts the selected columns before C1 (pushing other columns to the right).

- **After last column in use** places the selected columns after the last non-empty column.

- **Before column** inserts the selected columns before whatever column you click in the list box.

Naming, sizing, and hiding columns

▶ To name a column

1 Click a column name cell.

2 Type the name. Names cannot:

- be longer than 31 characters

- begin or end with a space

- include the symbol ' or #

- start with or consist entirely of the symbol *

3 Press (Enter).

▶ To change the width of one or more columns

1 Select the column(s).

2 With your mouse, point to the top of a line dividing a selected column from another column. The cursor becomes a two-sided arrow ◀▮▶.

3 Drag the border until the columns are the desired width.

▶ To change the widths of all columns

1 Choose **Editor ➤ Column ➤ Standard Width**.

2 In **Standard column width**, enter a number.

3 Check the option **Change widths that were set individually**. Click **OK**.

▶ To hide and unhide columns

If you have many columns of data spread out over a worksheet and you want to more easily view relevant data, you may want to hide columns with less relevant data, or hide any empty columns. You can hide and unhide columns manually or through the Hide/Unhide Columns dialog box.

1 Make sure the worksheet is active and choose **Editor ➤ Column ➤ Hide/Unhide Columns**.

2 Select the columns you wish to hide and move them to **Hidden Columns** with ▶, or use ▶▶ to move all columns.

3 Unhide columns by moving them to **Unhidden Columns**.

4 If you like, you have the option, using **Columns to display in list boxes**, to display all columns, data columns, or empty columns in the **Unhidden/Hidden Columns** list boxes. Click **OK**.

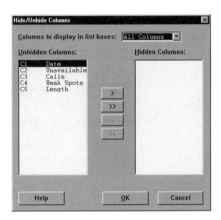

▶ To find and replace text, numbers, or date/time strings

1 With the Data window active, choose **Editor ➤ Replace**.

2 In **Find what**, type the text, number, or date/time string you want to search for. In **Replace with**, type the replacement text, number, or date/time string.

3 Click **Find Next**.

4 If the string you want to replace is found, click **Replace** or **Replace All**. If you do not want to replace this particular item, click **Find Next**.

Changing Column Data Types and Formats

There are three *types* of data: numeric, text, and date/time. A column can contain only one type of data. You can assign a data type to an empty column and change the data type of existing columns of data.

Once a column has a data type, you can specify format characteristics for that column. When you modify the format characteristics of a column, you are only changing the way that column is displayed in the Data window and graphs—you are not modifying the underlying value.

For example, say that a cell contains the number 1.2345678. If you change the format to display only two decimals, the Data window cell will display 1.23, the label for that data point on a graph will display 1.23, but all calculations will still use 1.2345678. The Session window output for analysis commands will display the format used by that command, regardless of the Data window format.

You can also create descriptions for columns, and select the fonts you want to use to display labels and data in the Data window.

Changing column data types

▶ **To apply a data type to an empty column**

1 Choose **Editor** ➤ **Format Column**.

2 Choose **Numeric**, **Text**, or **Date/Time**.

▶ **To change the data type of a non-empty column**

1 Choose **Manip** ➤ **Change Data Type**.

2 Choose the conversion type you want.

3 Complete the dialog box and click **OK**.

Changing numeric and date/time formats

▶ **To change the number of decimals displayed in a numeric column**

1 Select one or more columns. The columns must be empty (unformatted) or already in numeric format.

2 Choose **Editor** ➤ **Format Column** ➤ **Numeric**.

3 Select **Fixed decimal with _____ decimal places**.

4 In the text box, type the number of decimals and click **OK**.

▶ **To change the way the date and time are displayed in a date/time column**

A single date/time value can be a date, a time, or both. For example, all of the following are valid date/time values:

1/1/96
3:04 PM
1/1/96 3:04 PM

1 Select one or more columns. The columns must be empty (unformatted) or already in a date/time format.

2 Choose **Editor** ➤ **Format Column** ➤ **Date/Time**.

3 From the **Date/Time Column Format** box, select a format and click **OK**.

More | If you do not see a format you like in the Date/Time Column Format list, you can create your own in the **New format** text box. See Help for details.

Setting column descriptions and Data window fonts

▶ **To create or edit a column description**

Descriptions are useful for recording the source of the column's data, or for recording how the data have been modified from the source.

1 Choose **Editor** ➤ **Set Column** ➤ **Description**.

2 Type or paste the information you want, then click **OK**.

Note | Columns with descriptions have a red triangle displayed in the upper right corner of their column name cell. Column descriptions can be viewed in the Columns folder of the Project Manager.

▶ **To change Data window fonts**

You can set the font for labels (column numbers, like C1, column names, and row numbers), and one font for data (values in the cells).

1 Choose **Editor** ➤ **Worksheet** ➤ **Select Data Font** or **Select Label Font**.

2 Set font properties, then click **OK**.

Subsetting and Splitting Data

Often you will want to perform analyses or create graphs for a group of observations within a larger data set. For example, you may want to focus only on the females in the study, or only on the sales revenue for a certain quarter. MINITAB can create a worksheet that contains only the subset you want; when you make that worksheet active, subsequent analyses or graphs will reflect only that subset.

You can subset a worksheet based on conditions, or split a worksheet based on all the groups in a specified variable.

Subsetting based on conditions

You can subset your data based on one or more conditions. For example, you could create a subset based on two conditions: quarterly sales revenues that are greater than 100 (in thousands of dollars) *and* quarterly advertising expenses that are less than 15 (also in thousands). The rows of data that meet both those conditions are copied into a new worksheet. The original worksheet will remain.

Original worksheet				Subset in a new worksheet		
Quarter	Sales	Advertis		Quarter	Sales	Advertis
1	94	17		3	113	13
2	99	10		4	108	14
3	98	9				
4	92	22				
1	106	24				
2	116	18				
3	113	13				
4	108	14				

▶ **To subset based on conditions**

1 Choose **Manip** ➤ **Subset Worksheet**.

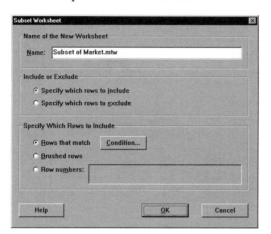

MINITAB automatically supplies a default name for the new worksheet, but you can change it if you like.

2 Under **Specify Which Rows to Include/Exclude**, choose **Rows that match** and click **Condition**.

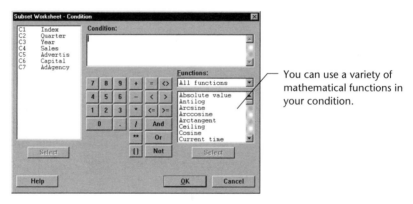

You can use a variety of mathematical functions in your condition.

3 In **Condition**, enter an equation which describes the condition. For example, to create a subset that contains only sales revenue higher than 100, you would enter:
Sales > 100

Note that if you chose in the Subset main dialog box to *exclude* rows, this equation would create a subset that would contain all the sales values that were *not* greater than 100.

4 Click **OK** in each dialog box.

Splitting a worksheet by groups in a variable

You can *split* a worksheet into groups based on all the unique values in a variable. For example, say that you have a worksheet of sales data with two columns: the column Sales contains the total dollars in revenue for a fiscal quarter, and the column Quarter contains the quarter in which the sales figure occurred (1, 2, 3, or 4).

If you split the worksheet based on the variable Quarter, MINITAB will create four new worksheets: one in which all values in Quarter equal 1, one in which all the values in Quarter equal 2, and so on. The original worksheet will remain.

▶ To split a worksheet by groups in a variable

1 Choose **Manip ➤ Split Worksheet**.

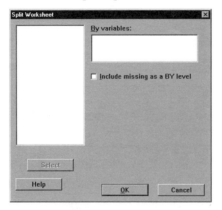

If you check **Include missing as a BY level**, MINITAB will create an additional worksheet if any of the columns in **By variables** contain missing values.

2 In **By variables**, enter one or more columns that contain the desired groups. Click **OK**.

If you enter multiple columns, MINITAB will create a new worksheet for each unique combination of values. For example, say that the column Year contains two groups, 1991 and 1992, and the column Quarter contains four groups, 1, 2, 3, and 4. If you entered Year and Quarter in **By variables**, MINITAB would create eight new worksheets, one for each quarter in 1991, and one for each quarter in 1992.

Stacking Columns or Rows

Sometimes you may need to combine two variables so you can analyze them with one command. MINITAB lets you easily stack the contents of columns, blocks of columns, or rows on top of each other. You can store the stacked contents in another column, preserving the original columns or rows, or store the stacked contents in a new worksheet.

When you stack column or rows, you also can create a column of subscripts, or identifier codes, that indicate which columns or rows an observation came from. Identifier codes can be used later to subset your data, to create graphs in which data points are displayed differently depending on which group they are from, or to unstack the columns.

For example, the Stacked column below contains the contents of Pulse1 stacked on the contents of Pulse2. We know that the value 88 comes from the second column (Pulse2) because the subscript is 2.

```
Pulse1  Pulse2  Stacked  Subscripts
    64      88       64           1
    58      70       58           1
    62      76       62           1
    66      78       66           1
    64      80       64           1
                     88           2
                     70           2
                     76           2
                     78           2
                     80           2
```

▶ To stack columns

1 Choose **Manip ➤ Stack ➤ Stack Columns**.

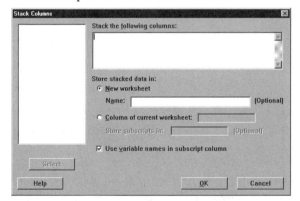

2 In **Stack the following columns**, enter the columns that contain the data you want to stack. The first column is stacked on top of the second column, the second on top of the third, and so on.

3 Under **Store the stacked data in**, choose the location for the new stacked data:

- choose **New worksheet** to place the stacked column into a separate worksheet

- choose **Column of current worksheet** to place the stacked column in the current worksheet in the column you specify. Click **OK.**

More | You can split a column into two columns using the command **Manip ➤ Unstack Columns.** For details, see Help.

Recoding Data

You can convert a value to another value, or convert a range of values to another value. You can recode numeric values to other numeric values (for example, converting all values from 1.0 to 1.9 to the value 1), text to text, text to numeric, or numeric to text.

For example, you could convert the data in the variable Sex from 1's and 2's to the words "Male" and "Female." The text values could be stored in a column named Gender.

```
Sex     Gender
 1      Male
 2      Female
 2      Female
 1      Male
```

▶ **To recode numeric data to text data**

1 Choose **Manip** ➤ **Code** ➤ **Numeric to Text**.

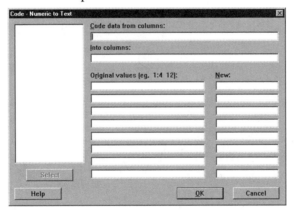

2 In **Code data from columns**, enter one or more columns, such as the column Sex.

3 In **Into columns**, enter one or more new or existing columns.

For example, if there is not a column named Gender, typing "Gender" would create a new column with that name.

4 In the first box under **Original values**, type a numeric value (for example, *1*) or range of values (for example, *1:12*, which means from 1 to 12).

5 In the first box under **New**, type the text value that the numeric value should be converted to. For example, to correspond to a value of 1 in the column Sex, you would type the word "Male." Do not include quotation marks.

6 Optionally, specify up to four other recodings in the remaining boxes, with a **New** value for every **Original** value.

Using the Calculator

The Calculator lets you quickly perform basic arithmetic or complex mathematical functions. The results of the calculation can be stored in a column or constant.

▶ To use the calculator

1 Choose **Calc ➤ Calculator**.

2 In **Store result in variable**, enter a new or existing column or constant.

3 In **Expression**, select variables and functions from their respective lists, and click calculator buttons for numbers and arithmetic functions. You can also type the expression.

4 Click **OK**.

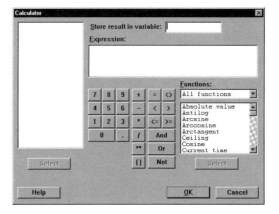

▷ Example of creating a column based on a calculation

In a study about pulse rates, you have two columns which contain the pulse rates of participants: Pulse1 and Pulse2. You can create a new column which is the difference between those two columns.

1 Open the worksheet PULSE.MTW.

2 Choose **Calc ➤ Calculator**.

3 In **Store result in variable**, type *PulseDif*.

4 In **Expression**, enter the equation *Pulse2 - Pulse1*. You can type the equation, or click on variables in the list box and buttons on the calculator.

5 Click **OK**.

Data window output

Pulse2	Pulse1	PulseDif
88	64	24
70	58	12
76	62	14
78	66	12
...	...	...

Interpreting the results

In the Data window, MINITAB creates the new column PulseDif, then stores the results there. The subtraction is done row by row.

More

MINITAB offers many other ways to manipulate and calculate data. For details on any of these topics, see Help.

Matrices

You can create matrices and do matrix algebra and other matrix operations: choose **Calc ➤ Matrices** and pick an item from the menu. Matrices can be stored by several commands, such as Regression, General Linear Model, Factor Analysis, and Cluster Analysis.

Random Data and Probability Distributions

You can generate random data with many different distributions, which is useful for simulations: choose **Calc ➤ Random Data** and pick a distribution name from the menu. You can also calculate probability densities, the cumulative probabilities, or the inverse cumulative probabilities of your data for a variety of distributions: choose **Calc ➤ Probability Distributions** and pick a distribution name from the menu.

Dynamic Data Exchange

Dynamic Data Exchange, or DDE, is a Windows protocol that allows applications to link to each other. Most often DDE is used to link data: when the data changes in one application, it is automatically updated in the other application. DDE can also be used to send and receive commands. In MINITAB you can even link Data window columns to other Data window columns; when one column changes, MINITAB can automatically recalculate the other column based on the changed values.

4

Using Data Analysis and Quality Tools

Data Analysis and Quality Tools Overview

MINITAB provides many statistical and graphical techniques to analyze data. Available methods include:

- basic statistics
- regression
- analysis of variance
- multivariate analysis
- time series
- tables
- nonparametric analysis

- exploratory data analysis
- power and sample size
- quality tools
- control charts
- reliability/survival analysis
- design of experiments

For a complete list of capabilities, see *Release 13 Capabilities Summary* on page xv. In addition, there is an overview topic in Help for each of the categories shown above. From there, you can move through the Help file to obtain information for a specific capability.

This chapter provides a sample of MINITAB's analysis capabilities including:

- basic statistics—descriptive statistics, one-sample t, and correlation
- regression—least squares regression
- analysis of variance—one-way ANOVA
- tables—cross tabulation
- control charts—$\overline{X}$ and R chart

More   MINITAB also provides many ways to graphically analyze your data. For more information, see Chapter 5, *Graphing Data* in this book.

Descriptive Statistics

MINITAB provides two commands, Display Descriptive Statistics and Store Descriptive Statistics, which calculate or store various statistics for each column or for subsets within a column. You can display these statistics in the Session window and optionally in a graph.

▶ **To display descriptive statistics**

1 Choose **Stat ➤ Basic Statistics ➤ Display Descriptive Statistics**.

2 In **Variables**, enter the column(s) containing the data you want to describe.

3 If you like, use one or more of the options listed below, then click **OK**.

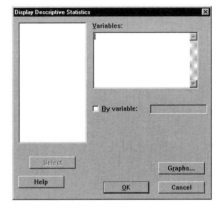

Options

■ display separate statistics for each unique value in a "By" column—see the example below

■ generate a histogram, a histogram with a normal curve, a dotplot, or a boxplot of the data in separate Graph windows, or display statistics in a single graphical summary

▷ **Example of displaying descriptive statistics**

You want to examine the weight (in pounds) of male (Sex = 1) and female (Sex = 2) students who participated in a pulse study.

1 Open the worksheet PULSE.MTW.

2 Choose **Stat ➤ Basic Statistics ➤ Display Descriptive Statistics**.

3 In **Variables**, enter *Weight*.

4 Check **By variable** and enter *Sex* in the text box. Click **OK**.

Session
window
output

Descriptive Statistics: Weight by Sex

Variable	Sex	N	Mean	Median	TrMean	StDev
Weight	1	57	158.26	155.00	157.61	18.64
	2	35	123.80	122.00	123.74	13.37

Variable	Sex	SE Mean	Minimum	Maximum	Q1	Q3
Weight	1	2.47	123.00	215.00	145.00	170.00
	2	2.26	95.00	150.00	115.00	131.00

Interpreting the results

MINITAB displays descriptive statistics for the variable Weight in the Session window. Because you used the "By variable" Sex, there is one description for males (Sex = 1) and one description for females (Sex = 2). Not surprisingly, the results show that males (mean = 158.26) weigh more than females (mean = 123.80).

Confidence Intervals and Tests of the Mean

MINITAB provides commands for calculating confidence intervals and performing tests of the mean for one or two samples. Capabilities include a Z-test, one-sample t-test, two-sample t-test, and paired t-test.

MINITAB also provides methods for the evaluation of proportions and differences in proportions. In addition, MINITAB provides methods to calculate confidence intervals and perform hypothesis tests for the median when you cannot assume that your data is normally distributed.

A one-sample t-confidence interval and hypothesis test for the mean are shown below.

▶ To compute a t-confidence interval and test of the mean

1 Choose **Stat ➤ Basic Statistics ➤ 1-Sample t**.

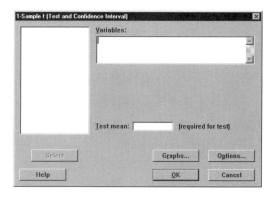

2 In **Variables**, enter the column(s) containing the samples. MINITAB performs a separate analysis on the data in each column.

3 To perform a hypothesis test, enter the value you would like to test against in **Test mean**. That is, enter the value of the mean under the null hypothesis.

4 If you like, use one or more of the options listed below, then click **OK**.

Options

- specify a confidence level for the confidence interval. The default is 95%.

- define the alternative hypothesis by choosing less than (lower-tailed), not equal (two-tailed), or greater than (upper-tailed). The default is a two-tailed test.

- display a histogram, dotplot, and boxplot for each response.

☞ Example of a t-confidence interval

Say that you want to obtain a 95% t-confidence interval for the mean resting pulse of a sample population.

1 Open the worksheet PULSE.MTW.

2 Choose **Stat ➤ Basic Statistics ➤ 1-Sample t**.

3 In **Variables**, enter *Pulse1*. Click **OK**.

Session window output

One-Sample T: Pulse1

```
Variable        N     Mean    StDev   SE Mean       95.0% CI
Pulse1         92    72.87    11.01      1.15  (  70.59,   75.15)
```

Interpreting the results

Based on this output, you estimate the mean resting pulse to be 72.87, and you can be 95% confident that the true value falls between the upper and lower limits of the reported confidence interval (70.59 and 75.15).

Correlation

Use Correlation to calculate the Pearson product moment coefficient of correlation (also called the correlation coefficient or correlation) for pairs of variables. The correlation coefficient is a measure of the degree of linear relationship between two variables. The correlation coefficient assumes a value between −1 and +1. If one variable tends to increase as the other decreases, the correlation coefficient is negative. Conversely, if the two variables tend to increase or decrease together, the correlation coefficient is positive.

▶ **To correlate pairs of columns**

1 Choose **Stat ➤ Basic Statistics ➤ Correlation**.

2 In **Variables**, enter the columns containing the measurement data. If you enter more than two columns, MINITAB calculates the correlation between every pair of columns and displays the lower triangle of the resulting correlation matrix.

3 If you like, use either of the options listed below, then click **OK**.

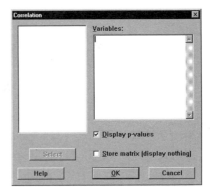

Options

- display the p-value for individual hypothesis tests. This display option is the default.

- store the correlation matrix. MINITAB does not display the correlation matrix when you store the matrix. To view the stored matrix, choose **Manip ➤ Display Data** or look in the Matrices folder in the Project Manager.

▷ **Example of a correlation**

Say you want to examine the relationship between the heights of students and their weights.

1 Open the worksheet PULSE.MTW.

2 Choose **Stat ➤ Basic Statistics ➤ Correlation**.

3 In **Variables**, enter *Height* and *Weight*. Click **OK**.

Session window output

Correlations: Height, Weight

```
Pearson correlation of Height and Weight = 0.785
P-Value = 0.000
```

Interpreting the results

The correlation value ($r = 0.785$; $p = 0.000$) suggests that height and weight are positively correlated. Further tests could explore the significance of this correlation and give you a better idea of the relationship between height and weight. For example, this correlation and the following regression examples use the combined male and female data. It may be better to subset the data by sex to determine if the relationship between height and weight differs for males and females.

More | To calculate Spearman's ρ (rank correlation coefficient), rank the data in both columns using **Manip ➤ Rank** and then use **Correlation** on the ranked data.

By using a combination of MINITAB commands, you can also compute a partial correlation coefficient, which is the correlation coefficient between two variables while adjusting for the effects of other variables.

Regression

Regression analysis is used to investigate and model the relationship between a response variable and one or more predictors. MINITAB provides various least squares and logistic regression procedures. Least squares procedures include simple, multiple, stepwise, and best subsets regression. You can also plot a fitted regression line and generate residual plots. MINITAB provides logistic regression methods for binary, ordinal, and nominal response values.

An example of the simplest form of regression, using the least squares method to fit a linear model, is shown on the following page.

▶ To do a linear regression

1 Choose **Stat ➤ Regression ➤ Regression**.

2 In **Response**, enter the column containing the response (Y) variable.

3 In **Predictors**, enter the columns containing the predictor (X) variables.

4 If you like, use one or more of the options listed below, then click **OK**.

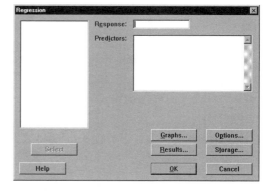

Options

- draw five different residual plots
- perform a weighted regression
- exclude the intercept (constant) term from the regression
- display the variance inflation factor (VIF), Durbin-Watson, and PRESS statistics
- perform lack of fit tests

- predict the response for new observations
- store various statistics for model evaluation or further analysis
- control the display of results

▷ Example of a simple linear regression

Suppose you want to explore the relationship between weight and height.

1 Open the worksheet PULSE.MTW.

2 Choose **Stat ➤ Regression ➤ Regression**.

3 In **Response**, enter *Weight*. In **Predictors**, enter *Height*. Click **OK**.

Session window output

Regression Analysis: Weight versus Height

```
The regression equation is
Weight = - 205 + 5.09 Height

Predictor        Coef      SE Coef         T        P
Constant      -204.74        29.16     -7.02    0.000
Height         5.0918       0.4237     12.02    0.000

S = 14.79      R-Sq = 61.6%      R-Sq(adj) = 61.2%

Analysis of Variance

Source             DF          SS          MS         F        P
Regression          1       31592       31592    144.38    0.000
Residual Error     90       19692         219
Total              91       51284

Unusual Observations
Obs     Height      Weight         Fit      SE Fit     Residual    St Resid
  9       72.0      195.00      161.87        2.08        33.13        2.26R
 25       61.0      140.00      105.86        3.62        34.14        2.38R
 40       72.0      215.00      161.87        2.08        53.13        3.63R
 84       68.0      110.00      141.50        1.57       -31.50       -2.14R

R denotes an observation with a large standardized residual
```

Interpreting the results

The p-value of 0.000 suggests that weight is a significant predictor of height, and the R^2 value of 61.6% tells you the amount of variability in the response that this model accounts for.

More | To work through an example of using regression, see Chapter 9, *Session Two: Doing a Simple Analysis.*

Analysis of Variance (ANOVA)

Analysis of variance (ANOVA) extends the two-sample t-test, which compares two population means, to a test that compares more than two means.

MINITAB's ANOVA capabilities include procedures for fitting one-way, two-way, and more complicated ANOVA models, a test of equal variances, and graphical procedures for viewing your data and understanding the fit of a model.

A one-way ANOVA tests for the equality of population means when classification is by single variable. Below, we show how to analyze data when the response data is in one column and there is a second column of level values identifying the population (*stacked* case). If you have data from each population in separate columns of your worksheet (*unstacked* case), you would use One-way (Unstacked).

▶ **To do a one-way ANOVA**

1 Choose **Stat ➤ ANOVA ➤ One-way**.

2 In **Response**, enter the column containing the response.

3 In **Factor**, enter the column containing the factor levels.

4 If you like, use one or more of the options described below, then click **OK**.

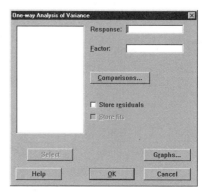

Options

- store residuals and fitted values (the means for each level)

- display confidence intervals for the differences between means, using one of the four multiple comparison methods:
  - Fisher's LSD
  - Tukey's
  - Dunnett's
  - Hsu's MCB (multiple comparisons with the best)

- draw boxplots, dotplots, and five different residual plots

▶ **Example of a one-way ANOVA**

1 Open the worksheet PULSE.MTW.

2 Choose **Stat ➤ ANOVA ➤ One-way.**

3 In **Response**, enter *Weight*. In **Factor**, enter *Sex*.

4 Click **Graphs**.

5 Check **Boxplots of data** and **Normal plot of residuals**. Click **OK** in each dialog box.

Session window output

One-way ANOVA: Weight versus Sex

```
Analysis of Variance for Weight
Source     DF        SS        MS        F        P
Sex         1     25755     25755    90.80    0.000
Error      90     25529       284
Total      91     51284
                                  Individual 95% CIs For Mean
                                  Based on Pooled StDev
Level       N      Mean     StDev   --+---------+---------+---------+----
1          57    158.26     18.64                            (--*-)
2          35    123.80     13.37    (---*--)
                                  --+---------+---------+---------+----
Pooled StDev =    16.84          120       135       150       165
```

Graph window output

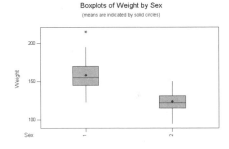

Boxplots of Weight by Sex
(means are indicated by solid circles)

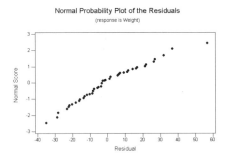

Normal Probability Plot of the Residuals
(response is Weight)

Interpreting the results

The analysis of variance output and boxplots clearly show that male and female weights are different. The high F-statistic and low p-value indicate there is a statistically significant difference between males and females. The 95% confidence interval for average weight of females is between about 118 and 130 pounds. For males, it is between about 155 and 162 pounds.

More | To work through an example of analysis of variance, see Chapter 10, *Session Three: Advanced MINITAB.*

Tables

Use MINITAB's table procedures to summarize data into a table or perform an analysis on tabled data. There are five tables procedures: Cross Tabulation, Tally, Chi-Square Test, Simple Correspondence Analysis, and Multiple Correspondence Analysis.

Cross Tabulation (shown below) displays one-way, two-way, and multi-way tables containing counts, percents, and summary statistics, such as means, standard deviations, and maximums, for associated variables.

▶ **To create a table of statistics**

1 Choose **Stat ➤ Tables ➤ Cross Tabulation**.

2 Do one of the following:

■ For raw data, enter two to ten columns containing the raw data in **Classification variables**.

■ For frequency or collapsed data:

  1 In **Classification variables**, enter two to ten columns containing the category data.

  2 Check **Frequencies are in** and enter the column containing the frequencies.

3 If you like, use one or more of the options listed below, then click **OK**.

Options

■ display the counts or percents of each cell within a two-way table

■ perform a χ^2 test of association for each two-way table

■ display the following for associated variables:
  – the mean, median, minimum, maximum, sum, and standard deviation for associated variables
  – the data, the number of nonmissing data, and the number of missing data
  – the proportion of observations equal to a specified value, and the proportion of observations between specified values for associated variables

■ display the marginals for selected variables

■ change the table layout

▷ **Example of a two-way table displaying column percents**

Suppose you want to summarize the data to obtain the number and percentage of smokers at each activity level.

1 Open the worksheet PULSE.MTW.

2 Choose **Stat ➤ Tables ➤ Cross Tabulation**.

3 In **Classification variables**, enter *Smokes* and *Activity*.

4 Check **Column percents** and click **OK**.

Session window output

Tabulated Statistics

ROWS: SMOKES   COLUMNS: ACTIVITY

	0	1	2	3	ALL
1	100.00	33.33	31.15	23.81	30.43
2	--	66.67	68.85	76.19	69.57
ALL	100.00	100.00	100.00	100.00	100.00

CELL CONTENTS --
                % OF COL

Interpreting the results

The rows are the Smokes variable: the 1's are those who smoke regularly while the 2's are those who do not. The columns are activity level: 1 = slight, 2 = moderate, and 3 = a lot (the 0 activity level is there because a value was entered by mistake by the person who recorded the measurements). A third of the slightly active students smoke while only a fourth of the very active smoke. Further analysis would be necessary to test whether this is a significant difference.

Quality Control

MINITAB offers a wide variety of quality control methods: control charts, quality planning tools, measurement systems analysis, process capability, and reliability/survival analysis.

Control charts, or statistical process control (SPC) charts, allow you to study the variation of a process over time. These charts plot a summary statistic (for example, a sample mean or a sample proportion) against the sample number.

The commonly-used $\overline{X}$-R chart is shown on the following page. As the name suggests, that chart is actually two charts in the same Graph window: a control chart for subgroup means (an $\overline{X}$ chart) and a control chart for the subgroup ranges (an R chart). Seeing both charts together allows you to track both the process level and process variation at the same time, as well as detect the presence of special causes.

Subgroup data can be structured in a single column, or in rows across several columns. When you have subgroups of unequal size, structure the subgroups in a single column, then set up a second column of subgroup identifiers.

▶ **To create an X̄-R chart**

1   Choose Stat ➤ Control Charts ➤ Xbar-R.

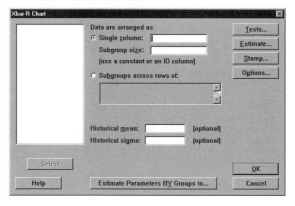

2   Do one of the following:

- When subgroups are in one column, enter the data column in **Single column**. In **Subgroup size**, enter a subgroup size or column of subgroup indicators.

- When subgroups are in rows, enter a series of columns in **Subgroups across rows of**.

3   If you like, use any of the options listed below, then click **OK**.

Options

- enter historical values for μ (the mean of the population distribution) and σ (the standard deviation of the population distribution) when you have a goal for μ or σ, or known parameters from prior data

- control the way MINITAB estimates μ or σ

- do eight tests for special causes

- place an additional row of tick labels, such as shifts or dates, below the subgroup numbers on the x-axis

- use the Box-Cox transformation when you have very skewed data

☛ Example of an $\overline{X}$ and R chart

A manufacturing plant that makes metal fasteners needs to evaluate their ability to keep their process on target (2.4 grams) with minimal variation in the weight of the fasteners. The fasteners are packaged in bags of five. They randomly selected 20 bags of fasteners and drew an $\overline{X}$ and R chart to evaluate the control of their production process.

1 Open the worksheet FASTENER.MTW.

2 Choose **Stat ➤ Control Charts ➤ Xbar-R**.

3 In **Single column**, enter *Weights*. In **Subgroup size**, type 5.

4 In **Historical mean**, enter 2.4. Click **OK**.

Session window output

Xbar/R Chart: Weights

```
Test Results for Xbar Chart
TEST 1. One point more than 3.00 sigmas from center line.
Test Failed at points: 10

Test Results for R Chart
```

Graph window output

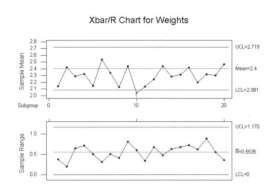

Xbar/R Chart for Weights

Interpreting the results

The test for special causes indicates that only one bag had a mean weight that was below the lower control limit (3 standard deviations below the target value). However, you will notice that many of the points fall below the center line suggesting that the process is creating fasteners that are often below the target value. The plant's quality control engineer may want to perform additional tests for special causes and re-evaluate this process.

None of the subgroup ranges are out of control.

What Next?

This chapter barely scratched the surface of MINITAB's analysis capabilities. You also have access to a host of procedures in a wide range of statistical areas: multivariate analysis, nonparametrics, time series, exploratory data analysis, design of experiments (DOE), and graphical analyses.

Some procedures in these areas are discussed in the sample sessions elsewhere in this book. Chapter 12, *Session Five: Designing an Experiment*, for example, is a sample session devoted entirely to the basics of DOE.

For more information on graphics, see Chapter 5, *Graphing Data* in this book.

For complete details on other procedures, see Help.

5
Graphing Data

Graphing Data Overview

In MINITAB, you can work with graphs in many ways:

- **Create graphs** from the graph menu commands or from options in analysis commands. You can create any one of four types of graphs.

- **Manage the graphs** in Graph windows. Each graph is displayed in a separate Graph window. You can have up to 100 Graph windows open at once. The **Window** menu lists each one, and the Project Manager Graphs folder lets you rename, arrange, and discard graphs.

- **Edit the graphs** with point-and-click ease, using the variety of options on the Tool and Attribute palettes. You can change almost every aspect of the graph's appearance.

- **Brush the data points in graphs** to see the corresponding values from the worksheet. This is a great way to interactively discover the meaning of your data.

- **Save and print the graphs** the way you would any MINITAB window. When you save your project, all open Graph windows are saved along with it. You can also save graphs individually, in a variety of formats. Or, you can copy and paste graphs into other applications.

Tip | There are lots of graph examples in this book, in the user's guides, and in Help.

Four Types of Graphs

You can create four types of MINITAB graphs: Core Graphs, Specialty Graphs, 3D Graphs, and Character Graphs.

Graph type	Definition	Graphs
Core	The most common, simple types of graphs, such as scatter plots and charts, that can also use a variety of options to create a virtually unlimited number of two-dimensional graphs. For example, the Plot command can create a simple scatter plot, but you can change options to create line plots, area plots, projection plots, and more.	On the Graph menu: Plots Time series plots Charts Histograms Boxplots Matrix plots Draftsman plots Contour plots

Graph type	Definition	Graphs
3D	Three-dimensional graphs that display three variables at once, such as height, width, and depth. You can display symbols that float in a three-dimensional space, or surfaces that follow the rise and fall of your data. 3D graphs have options for controlling positioning, lighting, and rendering.	On the Graph menu: 3D plots 3D wireframe plots 3D surface plots
Specialty	"Pre-customized" graphs that automatically combine elements from core graphs to display data in unique or sophisticated ways. Some specialty graphs can be generated simply by selecting a checkbox in an analysis dialog box.	On the Graph menu: Dotplots Pie charts Marginal plots Probability plots On various menus: Interval plots Forecasting plots and more...
Character	"Typewriter-style" graphs formed from characters that display in the Session window.	On the Graph menu: Stem-and-leaf plots

In this chapter, you will see how to create a few core and speciality graphs. For more information on other graphs, see Help.

Creating Core Graphs

MINITAB's core graph commands let you easily create simple, common graphs. From that simple core you can add on a wide variety of graphics options to create complex, sophisticated graphs.

One of the most common and useful graphs is the scatter plot, which is created in MINITAB with the core graph command Plot. Below are the instructions for creating a basic scatter plot, followed by instructions on using some graphics options. Finally, there is an example of creating a scatter plot using those graphics options.

▶ **To create a basic scatter plot**

1   Choose **Graph ▶ Plot**.

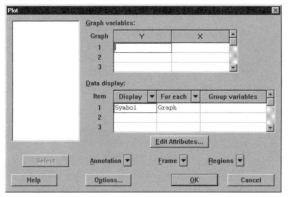

2   In first cell under **Y**, enter a variable.

3   In first cell under **X**, enter a variable. Click **OK**.

Data display elements and attributes

Data display elements are the graphical objects that represent data, such as symbols, bars, and connection lines. For example, in a scatter plot, each data point is represented by a symbol; on charts and histograms, each category is represented by a bar. In core graphs, you can change which data display elements to use on the graph. In the other types of graphs, many of the data display elements are already chosen for you.

Each data display element has *attributes*, such as size and color. You can change the attributes for all the data display elements in a graph, such as changing all the symbols to red. Core graphs offer you a lot of control over the appearance of data display elements.

▶ **To change the appearance of data display elements**

1   In a core graph dialog box, in the **Data display** table, click in the row of the element you want to affect.

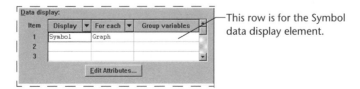

This row is for the Symbol data display element.

2   Click **Edit Attributes**. Change the settings for that data display element. For
    example, here is the Edit Attributes dialog box for symbols:

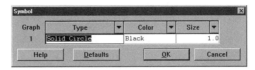

3   Click **OK**.

Displaying data differently for each group

You can also change the attributes for a group of data display elements, such as making
all the data points that have a certain value red, and all the data points that have
another value blue. In a core graph main dialog box, you specify a *grouping variable* —
a column which contains a list of values. MINITAB will create a different set of
attributes for each unique value in that grouping variable. See *Example of a scatter plot
with symbols in different colors* below.

▶ To make one group appear differently than another

1   In a core graph dialog box, in the **Data display** table, click in the row of the element
    you want to affect.

2   Next to **For each**, click the drop-down list and select **Group**.

3   Under **Group variables**, enter a variable.

▷ Example of a scatter plot with symbols in different colors

Say that you want to plot total sales figures versus advertising expenses. You would like
to easily see how the expenses differ for each year. In the marketing data set
(MARKET.MTW), the sales figures and advertising expenses are in the columns Sales
and Advertis, and the year in which those expenses occurred (1991 or 1992) is in the
column Year. By using Year as a grouping variable, you will make the data points that
occurred in 1991 appear as black solid circles, and the 1992 points as yellow solid
circles.

1   Open the file MARKET.MTW.

2   Choose **Graph ➤ Plot**.

3   In **Y**, enter *Sales*. In **X**, enter *Advertis*.

4   In the **Data display** table, choose **For each ➤ Group**.

5   Under **Group variables**, enter *Year*.

6   Click **Edit Attributes**.

7 First change all the symbols to use the same symbol type:

- Click the **Type** column header. This highlights all the rows in that column.

- Next to the **Type** column header, click the drop-down list and choose **Solid Circle**. Both rows will change at once.

8 Change 1992 circles to yellow:

- Under **Color**, click in the second row.

- From the **Color** drop-down list, choose **Yellow**.

9 Make the circle symbols twice as big:

- Click the **Size** column header. This highlights all the rows in that column.

- From the **Size** drop-down list, choose **2.0**. Both rows will change at once.

10 Click **OK** twice.

Graph window output

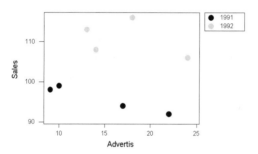

Creating Specialty Graphs

Using the core graph commands, you could create an incredible variety of two-dimensional graphs. The drawback is that for a complex graph, you might have to follow a large number of steps. With specialty graphs, the work is already done for you. The specialty graph commands let you specify just a few options to create useful, complex graphs.

Specialty graphs can be accessed in three ways:

- **On the Graph menu**. Specialty graphs that are applicable in a variety of statistical areas are found on the Graph menu.

- **On analysis menus**. Specialty graphs that are most often applicable to a single statistical area are found on the menu for that area. For example, residuals plots are often used in regression, so the command is accessed using the menu command **Stat ➤ Regression ➤ Residual Plots**.

- **As graph options in analysis dialog boxes**. Many graphs are created using the results of an analysis. Instead of storing results in the worksheet, then generating a graph from a menu command, often you can choose to display the graph as part of the analysis results. For example, when you perform a balanced analysis of variance, you can choose to create a histogram of the residuals and several other graphs: just open the Balanced Analysis of Variance dialog box, click **Graphs**, and select one or more graphs. When you execute the command, MINITAB will display text output in the Session window, and display the requested graphs in Graph windows.

▶ **To create a marginal plot**

The Marginal Plot command makes it easy to create a scatter plot that has another type of graph, such as a histogram, placed in the margins.

Example of a marginal plot with histograms

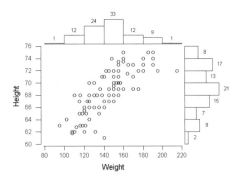

1   Choose **Graph ➤ Marginal Plot**.

2   Enter one column in **Y variable** and one column in **X variable**.

3   Under **Type of marginal plot**, choose **Histogram**, **Boxplot**, or **Dotplot**. Click **OK**.

Managing Graph Windows

You can have up to 100 Graph windows open at once. MINITAB provides a handy tool for arranging, naming, opening, and closing multiple Graph windows: the Graphs folder in the Project Manager.

▶ To manage graphs

1 Click on the **Show Graphs Folder** button on the Project Manager Toolbar.

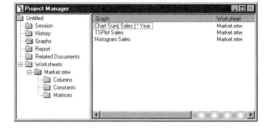

2 Click and drag in the Graphs folder to select the graphs you want to manage.

3 Right-click on the selected graphs and choose an action from the menu. The action will be applied to all the selected graphs, one at a time if necessary. For example, **Tile** arranges all the selected graphs at once; **Save As** tells MINITAB to prompt you to save each graph, one at a time.

Graph Editing

After you produce a graph in a Graph window, you can edit it. Graph editing is useful for putting text, lines, marker symbols, and polygons anywhere on an existing graph. You can also edit and change the attributes of objects generated with the existing graph. The graph editing tools, shown below, are often easier to use than the graph's options dialog boxes.

Use the Tool palette to create text, rectangles, ovals, lines, markers, and open and closed polygons.

Use the Attribute palette to change the color, size, and type of objects on the graph. You can change text, edges, fills, and symbols.

Note, however, that the changes you make with graph editing tools apply only to that particular Graph window, and do not affect the settings in the dialog box that created the graph. That means that if your data changes and you want to create a new graph, any changes you made to the first graph with graph editing tools would not be carried over.

For example, say that you create a plot with the Plot dialog box, then use the graph editing features to change all the plot's symbols from black to red. When you open the Plot dialog box again, the symbol attributes will still be set to black; when you click **OK**, a second Graph window will appear that contains a plot with black symbols.

▶ To enter Edit mode

1 Do one of the following:

   ■ Double-click the graph.

   ■ Make the Graph window active and choose **Editor ➤ Edit**.

Tip | When you enter Edit mode, the Tool and Attribute palettes should appear. If they do not, choose **Editor ➤ Show Tool Palette** or **Editor ➤ Show Attribute Palette**.

▶ To add a title

1 With the Graph window in Edit mode, click on the Text tool.

2 Drag an area where you want your title.

3 The Text box automatically appears. Type your title and click **OK**.

For example, you could add a title to the graph created on page 5-6.

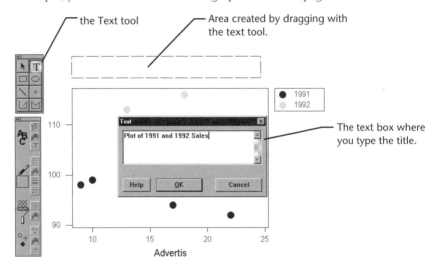

the Text tool

Area created by dragging with the text tool.

The text box where you type the title.

▶ To change the title size

1 With the Graph window in Edit mode, click on the title of the graph.

2 On the Attribute palette, click the Size tool.

3 Pick a size from the menu.

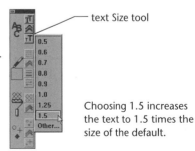

text Size tool

Choosing 1.5 increases the text to 1.5 times the size of the default.

More | Graph editing commands provide you with a full set of drawing, text, and coloring tools to modify your graphs as you wish when a graph is your active window.

Brushing Graphs

Graphs allow you to visually see the relationships between points. However, after you make a graph, you often want to learn more about a point, or a group of points. Brushing allows you to highlight points on a graph and see the corresponding observations (rows) in the Brushing palette and in the Data window.

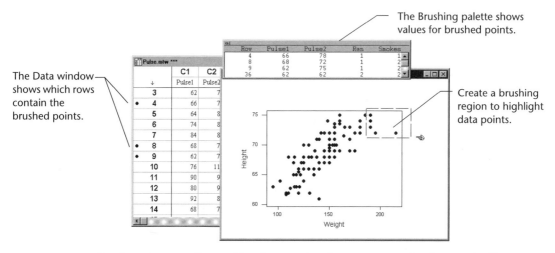

The Brushing palette shows values for brushed points.

The Data window shows which rows contain the brushed points.

Create a brushing region to highlight data points.

Brushing is especially good for showing the characteristics of outliers and telling whether points that lie in a brushing region share other characteristics.

Note | Some graphs cannot be brushed. You can only brush graphs that use symbols to represent individual data points, such as scatter plots or time series plots. Some specialty graphs also cannot be brushed because the symbols represent data that was created temporarily by the command; the data does not exist in the worksheet.

▶ **To brush a graph**

1   Make the Graph window active.

2   Choose **Editor ➤ Brush**.

3   Drag the ⇨ cursor over the points in the graph.

▶ **To add columns to the Brushing palette**

1   Choose **Editor ➤ Set ID Variables**.

2   Click **Use columns** and type the column names or numbers you want to display. Click **OK**.

Printing and Saving Graphs

Printing graphs

You can print a graph just as you would any other MINITAB window.

▶ To print a graph

1   With the Graph window active, choose **File ➤ Print Graph**.

Saving graphs

Saving the contents of a Graph window is similar to saving other MINITAB windows. When you save your project, all open graphs are saved as part of the project (see *Opening, saving, and closing projects* on page 1-10). You can also save or export graphs individually. The method you pick depends on your needs:

- If you want to view and edit that graph in other MINITAB projects, or if you want to view the graph in earlier releases of MINITAB, save the graph in a MINITAB Graphics Format (MGF) file. You can then re-open that graph in MINITAB.

- If you want to use the graph in another application, such as in Microsoft Word or on a web page, you can save the graph in a file format such as bitmap (BMP), JPEG (JPG), or TIFF (TIF).

- If you want to view *and* edit that graph in other Windows applications, you can copy and paste the graph. The graph is an OLE (pronounced "o lay") object that can be edited with MINITAB graph editing tools within the other application.

- If you want the graph to appear in a printed word processing document at the highest-possible resolution, you can print the graph to an Encapsulated PostScript (EPS) file. This creates an image that cannot be viewed in the word processing program, but will print at the best quality. For details, see Help.

▶ To save a graph

1   With the Graph window active, choose **File ➤ Save Graph As**.

2   In **Save as type**, choose the format that can be used by the other application. To use the graph in MINITAB, choose **Minitab Graph (*.MFG)**.

3   In **File name**, type a name and click **Save**.

▶ To open a graph

You can open a MINITAB Graphics Format (MGF) file, or open graphs that are contained in a MINITAB Project (MPJ) file.

1 Choose **File ➤ Open Graph**.

2 Under **Files of type**, select either MINITAB Graphics Format or MINITAB Project.

3 Select a directory and file name, then click **Open**.

4 If you select a MINITAB Project file, MINITAB then displays a list of the graphs in that project. Select a graph and click **OK**.

▶ To copy and paste a graph

1 With the Graph window active, choose **Edit ➤ Copy Graph**.

2 In the other application, choose the paste command.

Note | If the application is OLE compliant, the graph will be pasted as an OLE object you can edit with the MINITAB graph editor (below). If the application is not OLE compliant, the graph will be pasted as a Windows Metafile. Depending on the capabilities of the application, the Metafile will be pasted as a drawing whose parts (titles, lines, symbols, etc.) can be individually edited by that application's editing tools, or as a static bitmap.

▶ To edit a pasted MINITAB graph in another application

This option is only available if the application is OLE compliant.

1 Double-click the graph. The MINITAB Graph Editor window will appear.

2 Use MINITAB's graph editing tools.

3 Close the window. The changes will be reflected in the application.

Tip | With the OLE graph editor, you can also save a copy of the graph to a file: choose **File ➤ Save Copy As**.

6

Managing the Session Window and Generating Reports

Overview

The Session window displays the text output generated by your analyses.

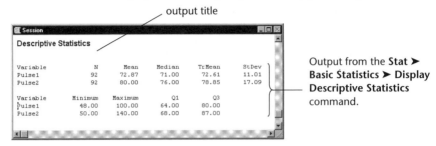

In the Session window you can

- navigate through the output (which can add up when you use the same project for a long time)

- edit and format text

- print and save text in different file formats (Session window text can then be used in a word processor or some other application)

More | The Session window can also display the command language used to generate the output, as well as provide a place to type session commands. For details on both these features, see *Executing Session Commands* on page 7-2.

Navigating in the Session Window

To view output, you can use the Session window scroll bars or use arrow keys just as you would in any window on your system. MINITAB also offers other ways to find output: the **Next Command** and **Previous Command** buttons let you jump to the output for each command. You also can use the Project Manager Session folder to jump to command output. The **Find** command lets you search for specific words or numbers in your output.

▶ **To move to command output if you are in the Session window**

1 To move forward (down) to the next block of output, click the 🔽 button on the Session window toolbar or choose **Editor ➤ Next Command**.

2 To move backward (up) to the previous block of output, click the 🔼 button on the Session window toolbar or choose **Editor ➤ Previous Command**.

▶ **To jump to command output from the Project Manager Session folder**

- In the Session folder, right-click on a command output title, and choose **Go To Title**.

▶ **To find words or numbers in the Session window**

1 With the Session window active, choose **Editor ➤ Find**.

2 In **Find what**, type the characters you want to search for.

3 Click **Find Next**.

More | MINITAB also has a feature for automatically replacing text—see *Finding and replacing text* on page 6-5.

Editing and Formatting Text

To do any editing or formatting in the Session window, you must first make the output editable (described below). Then you can do any of the following:

- Select text
- Change text or add comments
- Cut, copy, or paste text to other parts of the Session window, to the Data window, or to other applications
- Find and replace text

More | You can also change the fonts used in the Session window. For details, see Help.

Making output editable or read-only

The Session window is by default set to read-only. This means that output can be copied, but it cannot be deleted or modified. If you want to add comments, cut and paste text and numbers, or use the Replace feature (see *Finding and replacing text* on page 6-5), you can change the Session window output to editable. You can change modes back and forth throughout a session.

▶ **To change editing modes**

1 Choose **Editor ➤ Output Editable** to check or uncheck the menu item.

2 Check the menu item to make Session window output editable.

3 Uncheck the menu item to make Session window output read-only.

Selecting text

As well as the standard ways to select text in a Windows environment (such as dragging the mouse or using [Shift]+ a navigation key), the Session window offers three other methods that you may find useful:

▶

To select...	Do this
all the text in the Session window	Choose **Edit ➤ Select All**.
an entire line or group of lines	Drag along the left margin.
a rectangle (or column)	While holding down [Alt], drag the mouse to form a rectangle.

Tip | The rectangle selection option is especially useful for copying columnar output to paste into the Data window or a spreadsheet. For details, see *To copy Session window output to the Data window* on page 6-5.

Editing text

You can change and add text in the Session window just as you would in a Windows word processor.

▶ **To edit text in the Session window**

- To delete text, select the text, then press [Delete].

- To insert blank lines, press [Enter].

- To add comments, position the cursor wherever you want and type.

Note | If the comment is on a line by itself (and not on a line of output, or a line containing a title), the text will be in the comment font. For details on using fonts, see Help.

Cutting, copying, and pasting

You can cut, copy, and paste text just as you would in a word processor. You can exchange text with other applications, delete or move text in the Session window, or copy Session window output to the Data window.

When you copy text to the Clipboard, the text is copied in two formats: Text (ASCII or TXT), which has no fonts, and Rich Text Format (RTF), which retains fonts. If you paste into an application that understands RTF, the output will appear exactly as it does in MINITAB. If you paste into an application that does not understand RTF, the plain text will be pasted.

Tip | With plain text, the tables of output may not line up correctly in the other application. To make the output appear as it does in MINITAB, apply a monospace font, such as Courier.

▶ To copy Session window output to the Data window

1 Highlight the desired text in the Session window. To select a rectangle of output, hold down the [Alt] key while dragging with the mouse.

2 Choose **Edit ➤ Copy**.

3 In a Data window, place your cursor in the cell that is the top left corner of the area you want to paste to. Make sure there is enough room for the selection in the surrounding cells. If there is not enough room, the pasted data will overwrite the existing data.

Rectangular selection that is two columns wide and three rows long.

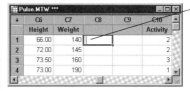
There is enough room to the right and below the active cell to paste the selection.

4 Choose **Edit ➤ Paste**.

5 A dialog box appears. Click one of the following buttons:

- To paste the data across columns (one value in the first column, one value in the next column, etc.), click **Use spaces as delimiters**.

- To paste all the data in one column, click **Paste as a single column**.

Finding and replacing text

▶ To find and replace text

1 Choose **Editor ➤ Replace**.

2 In **Find what**, type the text you want to search for. In **Replace with**, type the replacement text. You can type any combination of numbers and letters.

3 Click **Find Next**.

4 If the text you want to replace is found, click **Replace** or **Replace All**. If you do not want to replace this particular item, click **Find Next**.

Printing and Saving Text

Your session consists of everything you see in the Session window, such as tables of statistical results and comments you may have added. You can print all of the Session window or just a portion of it. You can also save the Session window text in different file formats.

Printing the Session window

▶ To print the entire window

1 Make the window active.

2 Choose **File ➤ Print Session Window** and click **OK**.

▶ To print a block of text

1 Select text in the Session window.

2 Choose **File ➤ Print Session Window**.

3 Under **Print Range**, make sure **Selection** is chosen. Click **OK**.

▶ To print command output using the Project Manager Session folder

1 In the Session folder, select one or more command output titles.

2 Right-click on the selected files and choose **Print.** Click **OK**.

Saving Session window contents

You can save the Session window contents in several formats.

▶ To save the contents of the Session window

1 Make the Session window active.

2 Choose **File ➤ Save Session Window As**.

3 Under **Files of type**, pick a file type:
   - Text (TXT) file—a plain text file that does not contain fonts, but is understood by every word processor and text editor.
   - Rich Text Format (RTF) file—a format that retains fonts and is understood by many word processors.
   - List (LIS) file—useful for longtime users of MINITAB, this option creates a plain text file with the extension LIS. The OUTFILE session command saves Session text with an LIS extension, and this option lets you create an identical outfile without using session commands.

4 Enter a name and click **OK**.

7

Session Commands and Macros

- Session Commands and Macros Overview, 7-2
- Executing Session Commands, 7-2
- Basic Rules for Typing Session Commands, 7-3
- Using Macros, 7-4

Session Commands and Macros Overview

Session commands are a useful alternative to menu commands, especially when you want to repeat a group of actions or create a macro.

What are session commands? Whenever you use a menu command, or click OK in a dialog box, MINITAB generates commands that describe the action. Most commands are simple, easy to remember words, like PLOT, CHART, or SORT. These session commands, collectively referred to as *command language*, are stored in the Project Manager History folder.

You can execute session commands to carry out actions immediately. Commands can be entered in two places: the Command Line Editor and the Session window. If you want to repeat a group of actions, you can copy commands from the History folder and paste them into the Command Line Editor or Session window.

If the group of commands are ones you want to repeat often, you can create a macro. A macro file can be saved, shared with others, and executed whenever you want. Macros can be simple and quick to create, or complex and sophisticated.

If you use session commands often, you will probably want to enable command language in the Session window. This will let you see the session commands along with your text output, and will also let you type session commands in the Session window.

Executing Session Commands

You can type commands in two places: the Command Line Editor and the Session window. The Command Line Editor is more convenient, but long-time users of MINITAB may be used to typing commands in the Session window.

▶ **To execute commands with the Command Line Editor**

1   Choose **Edit ➤ Command Line Editor**.

Paste, type, and edit commands here.

Use the scroll bars to see more commands.

2   Type the session commands—see *Basic Rules for Typing Session Commands* on page 7-3.

3   Click **Submit Commands**.

▶ **To execute commands in the Session window**

1 Make the Session window active.

2 Choose **Editor ➤ Enable Commands** so that **Enable Commands** is checked. If Enable Commands is already checked, you do not have to do anything.

3 Type the session commands at the MTB > prompt—see *Basic Rules for Typing Session Commands* below.

4 After each command or subcommand line, press [Enter].

▶ **To repeat a block of commands**

1 Click the History button [≥] on the Project Manager Toolbar to bring up the History folder.

2 Click and drag the bounding box in the History folder until you have selected a block of commands. Right-click on the selected commands and choose **Copy**.

3 In the Command Line Editor, or at the Session window's MTB > prompt, press [Ctrl]+[V].

4 In the Command Line Editor, click **Submit Commands**. In the Session window, press [Enter].

More | To work through an example of quickly repeating an analysis using this method, see Chapter 10, *Session Three: Advanced MINITAB.*

▶ **To show session commands along with output**

1 Select **Editor ➤ Enable Commands** so that **Enable Commands** is checked. If Enable Commands is already checked, you do not have to do anything.

Basic Rules for Typing Session Commands

Command order and punctuation

Type commands in this order:

1 Type the main command, followed by any arguments. No extra text is allowed on the command line. If you are going to use subcommands, end the main command line with a semicolon.

2 Type any subcommands and any subcommand arguments, ending each line with a semicolon.

3 With the last subcommand, end the line with a period.

Specifying arguments

Arguments can be variables (columns, stored constants, and matrices), text strings, or numbers (constants).

Variables

- Enclose variable names in single quotation marks
  (for example, HISTOGRAM 'Salary').

- Variable names and variable numbers are interchangeable. For example, the two following commands do the same thing (if C1 is named 'Sales'):
  DESCRIBE C1 C2
  DESCRIBE 'Sales' C2

- Specify a range of variables by using a hyphen between the first and last variables you want. For example, PRINT C2-C5 is equivalent to PRINT C2 C3 C4 C5. If C2 was named Sales and C5 was named Costs, you could also type PRINT 'Sales'-'Costs'.

Text strings and numbers

- enclose text strings (such as file names or titles) in double quotes, as in
  TITLE "This Is My Title"

- do not enclose numbers in quotes unless you want the number to appear as text.

- To specify a range of numbers, abbreviate a sequence by using the following conventions:

1:4	expands to	1 2 3 4
4:1	expands to	4 3 2 1
1:3/.5	expands to	1 1.5 2 2.5 3

More | For more options and syntax variations of session commands, see the Session Command Help file.

Using Macros

Macros are made up of session commands that are stored in a file. There are three types of macros you can use in MINITAB, ranging from the simple to the complex: Execs, global macros, and local macros. This section discusses how to create and invoke Execs, but you should know about all three types in case you want to create more sophisticated macros.

Execs, the simplest macros, are simply collections of commands that execute one after another, and work as long as the input data are always in the same columns and the output data can go in the same columns.

Global macros also need input and output columns to be located in the same place, but they are more powerful than Execs because they can use MINITAB's special macro commands. Macro commands allow the macro to do things like perform actions conditionally (for example, subtract C1 from C2 if C2 is greater than C1) or loop through commands a set number of times (for example, display descriptive statistics, subtract the highest number, then display descriptive statistics 10 times).

Local macros are the most complicated to create, but they are the most flexible and powerful. Not only can they use all the macro commands that global macros can use, but local macros can also act on whatever columns you specify, just like MINITAB session commands. So if in one worksheet your input data is in C1, and in another worksheet the data is in C7, you can use the same macro on both data sets; just specify C1 or C7 when you execute the macro.

Note | Global macros cannot invoke local macros. A number of MINITAB's menu commands are actually local macros. For example, the menu command **Stat ➤ Time Series ➤ Trend Analysis** invokes the local macro %TREND. So, if you want your macro to invoke local macros, create a local macro or an Exec.

The macro files used by MINITAB menu commands are stored in the Macros subdirectory under your main MINITAB directory. You can get ideas for your own macros by looking at the code in those files.

Creating an Exec

▶ To create an Exec

1 Perform your analysis, using menu commands or session commands as you prefer.

2 In the History folder, select the desired session commands and choose **Edit ➤ Copy**.

3 Open a text editor, such as Windows Notepad. Paste the text.

4 Save the file as any name with the extension MTB, as in MYEXEC.MTB.

If you are using a word processor, make sure to save the file as plain text (ASCII or TXT format); do not use the word processor's native format.

▶ To invoke an Exec

1 Open the worksheet that contains the data that will work with that Exec.

2 Choose **File ➤ Other Files ➤ Run an Exec**.

An Exec can run once, or many times. "1" appears by default.

3 Click **Select File**.

4 Select the directory and file you want. Click **Open**. The Exec will run.

More about macros

For more details on using Execs, global macros, and local macros, choose **Help ➤ Session Command Help**.

8

Session One:
MINITAB Basics

Chapter 8

Overview of Session One

The story

Clones are genetically identical cells descended from the same individual. Researchers have identified a single poplar clone that yields fast-growing, hardy trees. These trees may one day be an alternative energy resource to conventional fuel.

Researchers at The Pennsylvania State University planted Poplar Clone 252 on two different sites: one site was by a creek with rich, well-drained soil, and the other site was on a ridge with dry, sandy soil. They measured the diameter in centimeters, height in meters, and dry weight of the wood in kilograms of a sample of three-year-old trees. These researchers want to see if they can predict how much a tree weighs from its diameter and height measurements.

Congratulations! You have been hired as data analyst for the project, and you will be performing the statistical analysis.

What you will learn

In Session One you will learn how to:

- open a worksheet
- enter and edit data
- save data
- compute some basic statistics
- perform arithmetic

- plot the data
- compute a correlation coefficient
- edit and add comments to the output
- print and save your results

Time required

About 30 minutes.

Step 1: Start MINITAB

To start MINITAB:
From the Taskbar, choose **Start ➤ Programs ➤ Minitab 13 for Windows ➤ Minitab**.

Step 2: Open a Worksheet

When you start MINITAB, you begin with a new, empty project. You can add data to your project in many ways, but the most common way is to open a worksheet. Note that you are only copying the data from the worksheet to the project; any changes that you make to the data added to your project will not affect the original file.

In this session, you will use the file POPLAR1.MTW. This file is one of the dozens of worksheets that are shipped with MINITAB. Most of these worksheets are in the Data subdirectory or folder.

1 Activate the Project Manager by choosing **Window ➤ Project Manager**, by pressing Ctrl + I , or by clicking the ▦ button on the Toolbar.

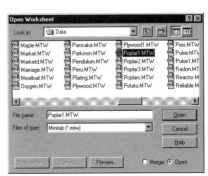

2 Right-click on the Worksheets folder in the Project Manager and choose **Open Worksheet**.

3 Make sure the file type is **Minitab (*.mtw)** and the current subdirectory is Data.

4 Click on POPLAR1.MTW and click **Open**.

5 If the Data window is not already visible, open it to view the columns in your worksheet: choose **Window ➤ POPLAR1.MTW** or press Ctrl + D .

This worksheet contains three variables, labeled Diameter, Height, and Weight. Each variable contains 15 observations—all the data collected so far.

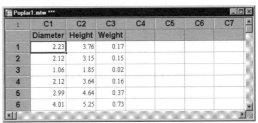

	C1	C2	C3	C4	C5	C6	C7
	Diameter	Height	Weight				
1	2.23	3.76	0.17				
2	2.12	3.15	0.15				
3	1.06	1.85	0.02				
4	2.12	3.64	0.16				
5	2.99	4.64	0.37				
6	4.01	5.25	0.73				

Step 3: Enter Data from the Keyboard

The worksheet POPLAR1 contained the data collected so far, but you just received new observations from the field, and there are five new rows to enter.

1 Press ⬇ until you reach the first blank cell in row 16 or, with your mouse, click on the first blank cell in row 16.

The Data window should look like this:

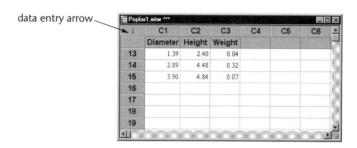

2 Make sure the data entry arrow points to the right. If it does not, click on it to change its direction.

3 Type the following from left to right across each row:

1.52	Enter	2.9	Enter	.07	Ctrl + Enter
4.51	Enter	5.27	Enter	.79	Ctrl + Enter
1.18	Enter	2.2	Enter	.03	Ctrl + Enter
3.17	Enter	4.93	Enter	.44	Ctrl + Enter
3.33	Enter	4.89	Enter	.52	Ctrl + Enter

Tip | **If you make a mistake:** click on or move to a cell (the contents will be automatically selected), type the correct value, and press Enter.

Step 4: Enter Patterned Data

You can always type data in the Data window, but if your data follow a pattern, there is an easier way to enter your data.

You now want to create a new variable that will indicate whether an observation was taken from the site with rich, well-drained soil (1), or from the site with dry, sandy soil (2). This new variable, called Site, will contain ten 1's followed by ten 2's.

2 Type *Site* and press ⏎Enter.

3 In row 1, type *1*.

4 Place your mouse over the square handle in the lower right corner of the selected cell. The crosshair cursor should change from white to solid black, which indicates that you are in Autofill mode.

5 Left-click and drag down to row 10. Autofill will automatically fill the selected cells with 1's.

6 In row 11, type *2*.

7 Click with the Autofill cursor and drag down to row 20.

The new Site column appears in the Data window and in the Columns folder in the Project Manager:

To view column
information, click on
the Columns folder
in the Project
Manager.

Step 5: Save Your Project

It is a good idea to save your work frequently. Now is probably a good time to save, since you have just entered new data.

1 In the Project Manager, right-click on the top-most folder (labeled Untitled) and choose **Save Project As...**.

2 In **File name**, enter *POPLAR1* for the name of your project. If you omit the extension .MPJ, MINITAB will automatically add it once you save the document.

3 Click **Save**.

4 If you see a message box asking if you want to replace an existing file, click **Yes**.

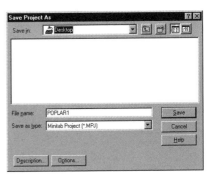

Step 6: Compute Descriptive Statistics

MINITAB offers a wide array of basic statistics to help you analyze your data, such as descriptive statistics, t-tests, z-tests, and correlations. You decide to produce summary tables and boxplots describing the variables Diameter, Height, and Weight for the trees at each site.

1 Choose **Stat ➤ Basic Statistics ➤ Display Descriptive Statistics**.

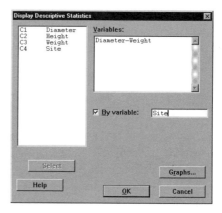

2 In the variable list box, click *Diameter* and drag the mouse so that you highlight *Diameter*, *Height*, and *Weight*. Then click **Select**.

3 Check **By variable**, and enter *Site*.

Checking **By variable** tells MINITAB to generate separate statistics for Diameter, Height, and Weight for each level of the variable Site.

Note   When you select a series of columns, MINITAB uses a dash to abbreviate the series. In this example, Diameter–Weight means the variables Diameter, Height, and Weight.

4 Click **Graphs**.

5 Check **Boxplot of data** and click **OK** in each dialog box.

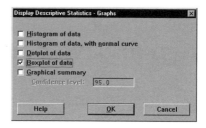

MINITAB displays text output in the Session window and each graph (three, in this case) in its own Graph window.

Session
window
output

Descriptive Statistics: Diameter, Height, Weight by Site

Variable	Site	N	Mean	Median	TrMean	StDev
Diameter	1	10	2.598	2.320	2.604	0.916
	2	10	3.028	3.250	3.041	1.284
Height	1	10	4.098	4.120	4.175	1.103
	2	10	4.255	4.865	4.351	1.254
Weight	1	10	0.3090	0.2050	0.2863	0.2528
	2	10	0.399	0.380	0.356	0.366

Variable	Site	SE Mean	Minimum	Maximum	Q1	Q3
Diameter	1	0.290	1.060	4.090	2.120	3.245
	2	0.406	1.180	4.770	1.488	4.053
Height	1	0.349	1.850	5.730	3.518	4.853
	2	0.396	2.200	5.540	2.775	5.143
Weight	1	0.0800	0.0200	0.7800	0.1575	0.4600
	2	0.116	0.030	1.110	0.063	0.648

Graph
window
output

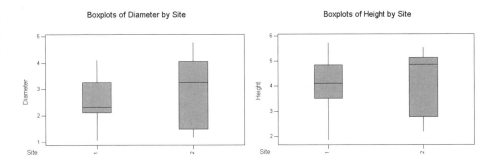

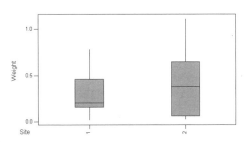

Tip You can tile the graphs to view all of them at one time on your screen: (1) press `Ctrl`+`I` and (2) click on the Graphs folder in the left pane of the Project Manager. The names of all the graphs will appear in the right pane. (3) Hold down `Ctrl` while selecting the desired graphs. (4) Right-click on your selection and choose **Tile**.

Judging from the boxplots, poplars grown at Site 2 are larger than those grown at Site 1. The Session window data confirm that the median values for Diameter, Height, and

Weight of the poplars are larger for Site 2 than for Site 1. Also, the variable Weight has a very large standard deviation relative to its mean. At Site 2, the minimum weight is only 0.03 kg while the maximum is 1.11 kg. It appears that some of our poplars are doing very well, while others are barely alive.

Step 7: Perform Arithmetic

Now on to the task of predicting how much the trees weigh. Based on previous work, the researchers have found that the weight of a tree is closely related to the square of its diameter multiplied by its height. Since you have diameter and height data, you can calculate this new variable using MINITAB's calculator. The calculator performs the equation you enter and puts the result in the variable you specify.

1 Choose **Calc ➤ Calculator**.

2 You decide to call the new variable "D2H" for diameter squared times height. In **Store result in variable**, type *D2H*.

3 In **Expression**, type *C1**2*C2*. Click **OK**.

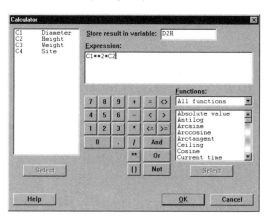

This expression tells MINITAB to square the variable Diameter (C1), multiply by the variable Height (C2), and put the result in a new variable called D2H.

Tip | You could also use the mouse to create the equation: (1) select *Diameter* from the variable list, (2) click the ∗∗, 2, and ∗ buttons on the calculator, and (3) select *Height* from the variable list.

The Data window shows the new variable D2H that you just created:

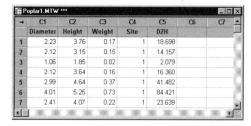

Now save the project changes.

4 Choose **File ➤ Save Project**, or press Ctrl+S or click 🖫 on the Toolbar.

Step 8: Create a Scatter Plot

The researchers have determined that there is a relationship between weight and D2H. You want to see if your poplars' data exhibit this relationship as well by plotting Weight by D2H on a scatter plot:

1 Choose **Graph ➤ Plot**.

2 In **Y** (the vertical axis), enter *Weight*.

3 In **X** (the horizontal axis), enter *D2H* and click **OK**.

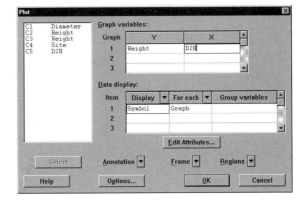

Graph window output

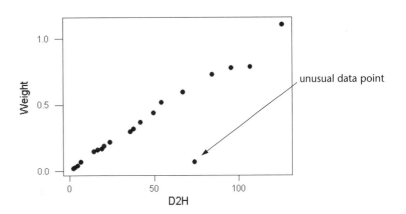

unusual data point

You see a positive linear relationship between Weight and D2H. That is, as D2H increases, so does Weight. You also notice an unusual data point—a tree that has a very low weight for a relatively high D2H value. For now, you decide to ignore it, but it is something you may want to check on later. Next, you will compute the correlation between these two variables to quantify the relationship.

Step 9: Compute a Correlation Coefficient

From the scatter plot, you have seen that as D2H increases, so does Weight. Now you want to measure the association between these two variables by computing a correlation coefficient.

1 Choose **Stat ➤ Basic Statistics ➤ Correlation**.

2 In **Variables**, enter *Weight* and *D2H*. Click **OK**.

Session window output

Correlations: Weight, D2H

```
Pearson correlation of Weight and D2H = 0.913
P-Value = 0.000
```

The correlation coefficient measures the linear relationship between two variables and assumes a value between −1 and +1. The high positive correlation coefficient of 0.913 is close to 1, thus quantifying the relationship that you already saw in the scatter plot— there is a strong linear association between Weight and D2H (diameter squared times height) for the trees in our sample.

Step 10: Edit the Session Window Output

It is time to create a report of your results: the text results, such as the summary descriptive statistics you computed, and the graphs, such as the scatter plot.

First you will edit the text output in the Session window to make it more appropriate for a report. You can edit text in MINITAB's Session window the same way you edit with a word processor, even finding and replacing text and changing fonts.

By default, the Session window is *read-only*, so that you cannot accidentally delete results. To begin editing, you will have to make the Session window editable:

1 Press <kbd>Ctrl</kbd>+<kbd>M</kbd> to make the Session window active.

2 Pull down the **Editor** menu.

- If there is no check mark next to **Output Editable**, then select it to enable Session window editing.

- If there is already a check mark next to **Output Editable**, then Session window editing is already enabled. Press <kbd>Esc</kbd> twice to close the menu.

Now you can edit your output.

3 Delete all the text above the Descriptive Statistics output and all the text between the Descriptive Statistics output and the Correlation output. Select the text by dragging over it with your mouse, then delete it by choosing **Edit ➤ Cut** or pressing <kbd>Delete</kbd>.

4 Scroll to the top of the Session window and type four comment lines as shown below:

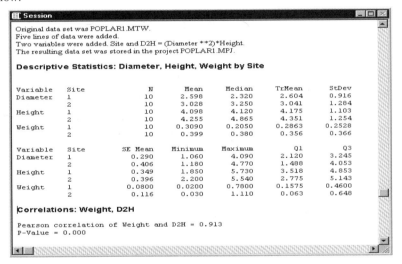

5 Save your work. Choose **File ➤ Save Project**.

The Session window is ready to print.

Step 11: Print Your Work

You will first print your output from the Session window, and then your graphs from the Graph windows.

1 With the Session window active, choose **File ➤ Print Session Window**, then click **OK**.

You could go to each Graph window and print them separately, but if you have more than one graph there is a faster way.

2 Press Ctrl + 1.

3 Click on the Graphs folder in the left pane of the Project Manager.

4 Click below the graph titles in the right pane of the Project Manager and drag up to select the four graphs you have created.

5 Right-click anywhere on the highlighted graphs and choose **Print**. Click **OK**.

Step 12: Save Your Work

When you save your project, you save all your work at once: all the data, all the output in the Session window, and all the open Graph windows. When you reopen the project, all that information will be waiting for you, right where you left it.

1 Choose **File ➤ Save Project**.

More   If you want to use output or data in another application or another MINITAB project, you can save your Session window output, data, and graphs as separate files. These separate files are copies of what is currently in your project—the contents of your project are not changed in any way.

Step 13: Exit MINITAB

If you want to take a break before continuing to another session, you can exit MINITAB.

1 Choose **File ➤ Exit**.

2 MINITAB may ask if you want to save changes to your project. Since you already saved your project above, there is no need to do it again here. Click **No**.

9

Session Two: Doing a Simple Analysis

Overview of Session Two

The story

Researchers at The Pennsylvania State University planted hundreds of poplar trees and grew them under a variety of controlled conditions. After three years, they measured the diameter in centimeters, height in meters, and dry weight of the wood in kilograms of a sample of trees.

You believe there is a close relationship between the dry weight of wood from young poplar trees and a variable that is a function of the diameter and the height of the trees. But what is that relationship?

These fast-growing, hardy trees may one day serve as an alternative source of fuel or chemicals. As data analyst for the project, you will determine if diameter and height measurements can be used to reliably predict the yield of wood.

What you will learn

In this session, you learn how to:

- use simple regression to find the relationship between the trees' diameter and height
- find and correct errors in your data, then quickly re-run your analysis
- generate graphs to visualize the relationship between variables
- customize the appearance of those graphs to make them more informative
- brush the graphs to identify key data points

Time required

About 30 minutes.

Step 1: Start a New Project

- If you are not already running MINITAB, start the program.
- If you have just completed Session One, start a new project: choose **File ➤ New**, click **Minitab Project**, and click **OK**.

If you have not saved your changes to the previous project, MINITAB will give you the chance to do so.

Step 2: Open a Worksheet

You will get data from a MINITAB saved worksheet named POPLAR2.MTW that is located in the Data subdirectory or folder.

1 Choose **File ➤ Open Worksheet**.

2 Move to the Data subdirectory and select the worksheet POPLAR2.MTW.

3 Click **Open**, then **OK** (if necessary).

Step 3: Perform a Simple Regression

Towards the end of Session One, you saw that as D2H (the diameter squared multiplied by the height) increases, so does Weight. One way to find out how well D2H predicts weight is to use a simple regression command:

1 Choose **Stat ➤ Regression ➤ Regression**.

2 In **Response**, enter *Weight*.

3 In **Predictors**, enter *D2H*.

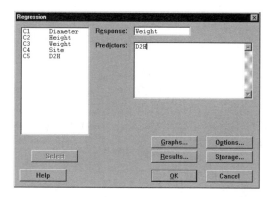

You decide you might as well do a series of plots for residual analysis to check for any potential problems.

4 Click **Graphs**.

5 Under **Residuals for Plots**, click **Standardized**.

6 Under **Residual Plots**, check **Histogram of residuals** and **Normal plot of residuals**.

7 In **Residuals versus the variables**, enter *D2H*.

8 Click **OK** in each dialog box.

MINITAB displays the text output in the Session window, and displays each of the three graphs in its own Graph window.

Session window output

Regression Analysis: Weight versus D2H

```
The regression equation is
Weight = 0.0196 + 0.00758 D2H

Predictor          Coef     SE Coef          T        P
Constant        0.01961     0.04566       0.43    0.673
D2H           0.0075838   0.0007994       9.49    0.000

S = 0.1298     R-Sq = 83.3%    R-Sq(adj) = 82.4%

Analysis of Variance

Source             DF          SS          MS         F        P
Regression          1      1.5155      1.5155     89.99    0.000
Residual Error     18      0.3031      0.0168
Total              19      1.8187

Unusual Observations
Obs      D2H      Weight         Fit      SE Fit    Residual    St Resid
 12      126      1.1100      0.9756      0.0717      0.1344       1.24 X
 15       74      0.0700      0.5779      0.0374     -0.5079      -4.09R

R denotes an observation with a large standardized residual
X denotes an observation whose X value gives it large influence.
```

Graph window output

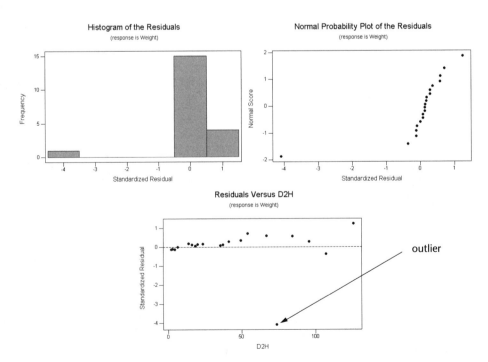

MINITAB displays the regression equation, the table of coefficients, the analysis of variance table, and—in the table of unusual observations—the identity of the outlier and influential observations (rows 12 and 15). Before proceeding with further analysis, you want to examine rows 12 and 15 to make sure they contain valid data.

A quick glance at the Residuals Versus D2H plot shows you that the data contains an outlier.

Step 4: Edit the Data

1 To view the worksheet, click on the Data window, choose **Window ➤ POPLAR2.MTW**, or press Ctrl + D .

2 Now go to the first unusual observation, in row 12 of the column named Weight:

   ■ Choose **Editor ➤ Go To**. (Select the first **Go To**).

   ■ In **Enter column number or name**, type *Weight*.

   ■ In **Enter row number**, type *12* and click **OK**.

The Data window now shows the 12th observation of Weight as the highlighted cell.

	C1	C2	C3	C4	C5	C6	C7	C8
	Diameter	Height	Weight	Site	D2H			
7	2.41	4.07	0.22	1	23.639			
8	2.75	4.72	0.30	1	35.695			
9	2.20	4.17	0.19	1	20.183			
10	4.09	5.73	0.78	1	95.852			
11	3.62	5.10	0.60	2	66.832			
12	4.77	5.54	1.11	2	126.051			
13	1.39	2.40	0.04	2	4.637			

Both Weight and D2H seem rather large, so you double-check the researchers' log sheets. It turns out that poplar #12 is a very healthy tree—the values are correct.

3 Click on the Weight value in row 15 to highlight it, or press ↓ three times.

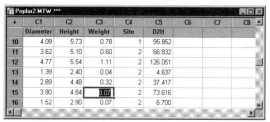

	C1	C2	C3	C4	C5	C6	C7	C8
	Diameter	Height	Weight	Site	D2H			
10	4.09	5.73	0.78	1	95.852			
11	3.62	5.10	0.60	2	66.832			
12	4.77	5.54	1.11	2	126.051			
13	1.39	2.40	0.04	2	4.637			
14	2.89	4.48	0.32	2	37.417			
15	3.90	4.84	0.07	2	73.616			
16	1.52	2.90	0.07	2	6.700			

Double-checking the log sheet shows that this value is actually an error. The correct value should be 0.70, not 0.07.

4 Type .7 and press (Enter).

The Data window should look like this:

	C1	C2	C3	C4	C5	C6	C7	C8
	Diameter	Height	Weight	Site	D2H			
10	4.09	5.73	0.78	1	95.852			
11	3.62	5.10	0.60	2	66.832			
12	4.77	5.54	1.11	2	126.051			
13	1.39	2.40	0.04	2	4.637			
14	2.89	4.48	0.32	2	37.417			
15	3.90	4.84	0.70	2	73.616			
16	1.52	2.90	0.07	2	6.700			

Poplar2.MTW ***

Step 5: Run the Regression Again

Now you are ready to run the regression again. Simply repeat the menu selection you made earlier. The Regression dialog box and Graphs subdialog box will contain the same settings as before. You are ready to go!

1 First, close all the graphs that you created before correcting the data. Choose **Window ➤ Close All Graphs** and click **OK**.

2 Choose **Stat ➤ Regression ➤ Regression** and click **OK**.

Tip | To set a dialog box back to its defaults, press (F3).

As before, MINITAB displays the text output in the Session window, and displays each of the three graphs in its own Graph window. First, look at the Session window output.

*Session
window
output*

Regression Analysis: Weight versus D2H

```
The regression equation is
Weight = 0.0200 + 0.00829 D2H

Predictor        Coef      SE Coef         T        P
Constant      0.01999      0.01365      1.46    0.160
D2H         0.0082897    0.0002390     34.68    0.000


S = 0.03880    R-Sq = 98.5%    R-Sq(adj) = 98.4%

Analysis of Variance

Source            DF          SS          MS         F        P
Regression         1      1.8108      1.8108   1202.89    0.000
Residual Error    18      0.0271      0.0015
Total             19      1.8379

Unusual Observations
Obs     D2H    Weight         Fit      SE Fit    Residual    St Resid
 12     126   1.11000     1.06492     0.02142     0.04508      1.39 X
 17     107   0.79000     0.90858     0.01740    -0.11858     -3.42R

R denotes an observation with a large standardized residual
X denotes an observation whose X value gives it large influence.
```

If you have a good model and have satisfied all the statistical assumptions, then you can measure the diameter and height of any poplar in this population and be able to predict its weight without cutting it down, drying it, and weighing it on a scale.

From the regression output, you see a high t-ratio and a low p-value for D2H in the table of coefficients, indicating strong evidence of a relationship between D2H and Weight. The large F-statistic and low p-value in the analysis of variance table quantify this relationship in a different way. The R^2 and adjusted R^2 values of greater than 98% further reinforce the assertion that there is a strong linear relationship between D2H and Weight.

Before making a final conclusion, however, you decide to look at the plots.

Graph window output

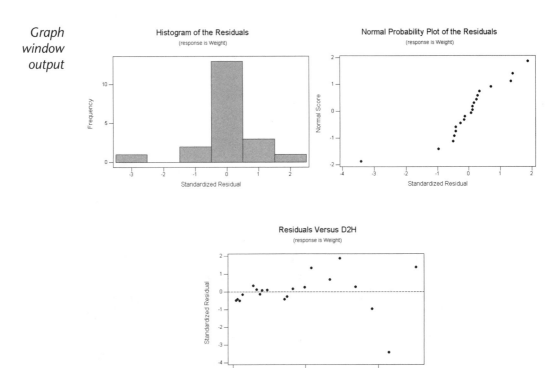

You notice from the Residuals Versus D2H plot that the variance does not appear to be constant—an important assumption for a regression model to meet. It is larger at bigger values of D2H. In the interest of time we will continue with our session, but this is something you would want to examine more closely.

Step 6: Draw a Fitted Regression Line

Next, you want to display a scatter plot with the regression line drawn on it to see how closely the measured data lie to the least-squares regression line.

To plot Weight versus D2H:

1 Choose **Stat ➤ Regression ➤ Fitted Line Plot**.

2 In **Response (Y)**, enter *Weight*.

3 In **Predictor (X)**, enter *D2H*. Click **OK**.

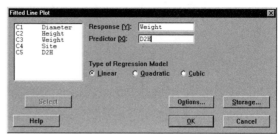

Graph window output

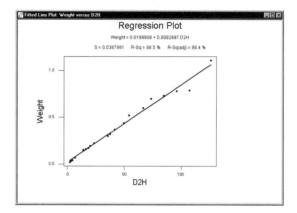

Step 7: Change the Graph Title

You would like to change the title of your graph. You could redo the dialog box and add a title in the Options subdialog box. Or, you can also edit the graph directly, after it has been created.

MINITAB's Graph Editor is very similar to most drawing packages. If you know how to use a drawing package, you should be able to edit MINITAB graphs very easily.

In this step, you will learn how to:

■ enter graph editing mode

■ change the text of the title

■ resize the text box so that the title fits on one line

Put the graph in edit mode

1 Make the Graph window active by clicking on it or choosing its name from the Window menu.

2 Maximize the Graph window.

3 Choose **Editor ➤ Edit**.

More A graph can be in one of three modes: *View mode* allows you to view your graph but nothing else, *Edit mode* allows you to edit your graph, and *Brush mode* allows you to identify data points. You choose the mode from the Editor menu.

4 Two palettes should appear. If they do not, open them:

- Choose **Editor ➤ Show Tool Palette**.
- Choose **Editor ➤ Show Attribute Palette**.

Your Graph window should look like this:

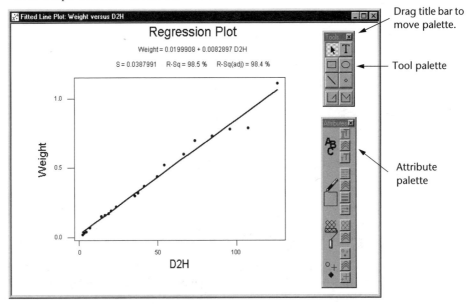

Your palettes may be in different positions. You can move a palette around the way you move a dialog box around—by dragging the title bar at the top of the palette.

Change the text of the title

1 On the Tool palette, click the selection tool [▶] if it is not already selected.

2 Click anywhere on the title and press Enter, or double-click on the title.

A text box containing the current title will appear on the screen:

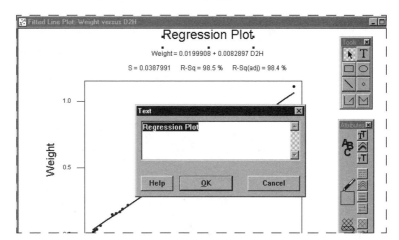

3 In the box, edit the title to say *Regression Plot for Poplar2 Data*. Click **OK**.

Resize the text box of the title

Because the title is longer, it is now on three lines. You need to resize the box that surrounds the title.

1 If necessary, click on the title to make it active. Handles will appear.

2 Place the cursor over the second handle up on the right edge. The cursor changes to crossed diagonal lines.

3 Click and hold the mouse button down and drag the right edge so the title is on two lines.

4 Place the cursor over the second handle up on the left edge. Click and hold the mouse button down and drag the left edge so the title is on one line.

Now you can position the title where you want it.

5 Put the cursor in the middle of the title.

6 Click and hold the mouse button down and drag the title to the position you want. Release the mouse button.

Step 8: Make the Regression Line Red

You decide to make the regression line red, so it is easier to see.

1 Click anywhere on the regression line. Handles will appear.

2 On the Attribute palette, click the line color tool ![icon]. A Color palette appears.

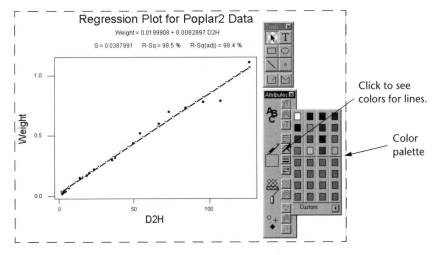

3 Click the red square. The line will become red.

4 Click in a blank space on the graph to remove the handles.

Step 9: Brush the Graph to Identify Points

One point has a very large value for D2H. You want to know what point this is. Brushing allows you to identify points on a plot. You will switch to Brush mode, and open the Brushing palette if necessary.

1 Choose **Editor ➤ Brush**. Your cursor will change to a hand.

2 If the Brushing palette does not appear (see below), choose **Editor ➤ Show Brushing Palette**.

3 Click on the point you want to identify. Its row number appears in the Brushing palette.

Brushing palette

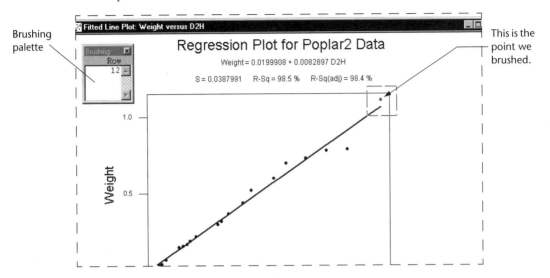

This is the point we brushed.

Suppose you would like more information on points you select. You can include data for up to ten worksheet columns in the Brushing palette.

1 Choose **Editor ➤ Set ID Variables**.

2 Check **Use columns**, then enter *C1–C4*.

3 Click **OK**.

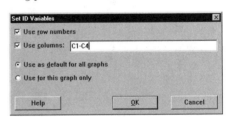

The Brushing palette widens to display the additional information. If you like, you can move it so both the palette and the plot can be easily seen.

You want to identify the two points on the extreme right of the plot. You can select a block of points by enclosing them in a rectangle. To draw the rectangle, you begin at the upper-left corner and drag down to the lower-right corner of the rectangle.

4 Move the cursor to the location where you want to begin drawing the rectangle. This location will be the upper-left corner.

5 Hold the mouse button down and drag down to the lower-right until the rectangle encloses the two points.

The points are enclosed in a rectangle and identified in the Brushing palette.

These are the points we identified.

These are the same points identified previously as being an outlier and influential observation. Here, brushing lets you quickly see the diameter, height, weight, and site information for these points.

The brushed points are also marked in the Data window.

brushed points

Step 10: Save and Exit

1 Choose **File ➤ Save Project**.

2 In **File name**, enter *POPLAR2* for the name of your project. If you omit the extension .MPJ, MINITAB will automatically add it once you save the project.

3 Click **Save**.

4 If you see a message box asking if you want to replace an existing file, click **Yes**.

5 If you want to take a break at this point, you can exit MINITAB by choosing **File ➤ Exit**, or you can go on to Session Three.

10

Session Three:
Advanced MINITAB

Chapter 10

Overview of Session Three

The story

How feasible are energy plantations? How much wood for energy can you realistically expect from these plantations, and how can you maximize yield?

In an effort to maximize yield, researchers designed an experiment to determine how two factors, Site and Treatment, influence the weight of four-year-old poplar clones. They planted trees on two sites: Site 1—a moist site with rich soil, and Site 2—a dry, sandy site. They applied four different treatments to the trees: Treatment 1 was the control (no treatment), Treatment 2 was fertilizer, Treatment 3 was irrigation, and Treatment 4 was both fertilizer and irrigation. To account for a variety of weather conditions, the researchers replicated the data by planting half the trees in Year 1, and the other half in Year 2.

As data analyst for the project, you will perform the statistical analysis on the sample data stored in the MINITAB file called POPLAR3.MTW.

What you will learn

In this session, you will learn how to:

- quickly generate basic statistics to describe the variables you are interested in
- change the codes the field researchers were using for missing values into missing value codes that MINITAB will recognize
- subset the data to focus on just the group of trees that you want to examine further
- create boxplots to see at a glance the differences between categories of trees
- use analysis of variance to determine which variables are contributing to the differences between trees

Time required

About 40 minutes.

Step 1: Start a New Project

- If you are not already running MINITAB, start the program.

- If you have just completed Session Two, start a new project: choose **File ➤ New**, click **Minitab Project**, then click **OK**.

If you have not saved your changes to the previous project, MINITAB will give you the chance to do so.

Step 2: Open a Worksheet

You will get data from a MINITAB saved worksheet named POPLAR3.MTW that is located in the Data subdirectory or folder.

1 Choose **File ➤ Open Worksheet**.

2 Move to the Data subdirectory and select the file POPLAR3.MTW. Click **Open**.

Two windows can show you information about this worksheet.

3 Choose **Window ➤ Project Manager** or press Ctrl + I.

If the left pane of the Project Manager is too narrow, simply click and drag the divider between the panes to the right.

4 In the left pane of the Project Manager, click on the Columns folder.

The right pane displays information about the data in the worksheet.

5 If the worksheet is not visible, open the Data window by pressing Ctrl + D.

The Data window shows you the columns of data in detail.

This worksheet contains seven variables: Site, Year, Treatment (experimental treatment), Diameter (cm), Height (m), Weight (kg), and Age (years).

	C1	C2	C3	C4	C5	C6	C7	C8
	Site	Year	Treatment	Diameter	Height	Weight	Age	
1	1	1	1	2.23	3.76	0.17	3	
2	1	1	1	2.12	3.15	0.15	3	
3	1	1	1	1.06	1.85	0.02	3	
4	1	1	1	2.12	3.64	0.16	3	
5	1	1	1	2.99	4.64	0.37	3	
6	1	1	1	4.01	5.25	0.73	3	
7	1	1	1	2.41	4.07	0.22	3	

Tip | If you want to adjust the column widths to fit the data, point with your mouse to the top of a line dividing two columns until the mouse cursor turns into a two-sided arrow. Then, press the mouse button down and drag the column border to make it wider or narrower.

Step 3: Generate Descriptive Statistics

You want to maximize yield, so you will focus on what factors influence the weight of trees. Begin by looking at the descriptive statistics for the variable Weight.

1 Choose **Stat ➤ Basic Statistics ➤ Display Descriptive Statistics**.

2 In **Variables**, enter *Weight*. Click **OK**.

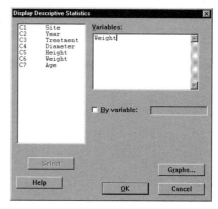

Session window output

Descriptive Statistics: Weight

Variable	N	Mean	Median	TrMean	StDev	SE Mean
Weight	298	1.099	1.640	1.994	10.255	0.594

Variable	Minimum	Maximum	Q1	Q3
Weight	-99.000	6.930	0.597	3.455

Notice the minimum value for Weight. It is certainly impossible to have a weight of −99 kilograms! The real story here is that our data gatherers in the field recorded the value −99 to represent a dead tree.

Leaving values of −99 in the worksheet is going to considerably throw off any analyses you do. In fact, it has already affected the output of the descriptive statistics just computed. The means and medians are artificially low, while the standard deviation is artificially high. You need to convert all −99's to missing values.

Missing values do not affect the results of any statistical analyses. MINITAB represents a missing value for numerical data with an asterisk (*).

Step 4: Recode the Data

MINITAB provides many data manipulation tools. One of the most useful is the Code command, which allows you change all the occurrences of one value into another value. In this case, you want to change all the −99's to *, the missing value symbol.

1 Choose **Manip ➤ Code ➤ Numeric to Numeric**.

2 In **Code data from columns**, enter *Weight*.

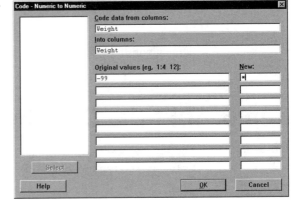

3 In **Into columns**, enter *Weight*. This will replace the old values in Weight with the new, coded values.

4 In **Original values**, type −99. This is the value you want to change.

5 In **New**, type *. This is the missing value symbol. Click **OK**.

In the Data window, you will see that all occurrences of the value −99 in the variable Weight have been replaced with *, the code for a missing data value.

Step 5: Tally the Data

How many trees of each age are you dealing with? Use the Tally command to find out:

1 Choose **Stat ➤ Tables ➤ Tally.**

2 In **Variables**, enter *Age.* Click **OK.**

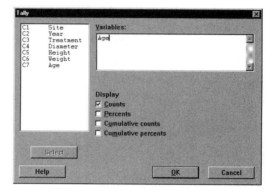

Session window output

Tally for Discrete Variables: Age

Age	Count
3	147
4	151
N=	298

The output shows that you have 147 three-year-old trees, and 151 four-year-old trees.

Step 6: Split the Data by Age

Suppose you want to analyze the data for just the four-year-old trees. Here is a technique you can use to create a new data set with just the four-year-old trees.

Make a separate worksheet for the four-year-old trees

1 Choose **Manip ➤ Split Worksheet.**

2 In **By variables**, enter *Age.* Click **OK.**

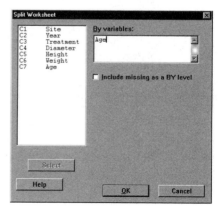

MINITAB will split the POPLAR3 worksheet using the values of Age. Since there are two unique values in the age column (3 and 4), MINITAB will create two new worksheets. The worksheet that contains the data for the three-year-old trees will be named POPLAR3.MTW(Age = 3); the worksheet that contains the data for the four-year-old trees will be named POPLAR3.MTW(Age = 4).

Rename the worksheet that contains the four-year-old trees' data

1 Press Ctrl + I.

2 In the left pane of the Project Manager, right-click on **POPLAR3.MTW(Age = 4)**.

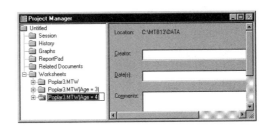

3 Click **Rename**.

4 Type *4YROLDS.MTW*.

5 Press Enter.

You will now perform the analysis on the four-year-old poplar data.

Step 7: Check for Normality with a Histogram

You will now create a histogram of the variable Weight.

1 Make sure the Data window named 4YROLDS.MTW is active. To make a Data window active, click on it, or choose its name from the Window menu. Notice that the active Data window has asterisks after its name.

2 Choose **Graph ➤ Histogram**.

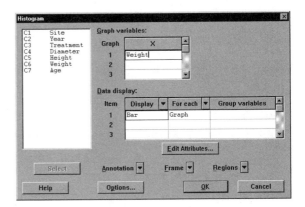

3 In **X**, enter *Weight*. Click **OK**.

The histogram appears in its own window.

Graph window output

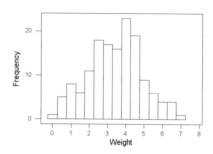

The weights of the poplars are approximately normally distributed (in a bell-shaped curve).

Step 8: Compare Weight by Treatment with Boxplots

Now you will want to look at the weight for each treatment. Boxplots are good for graphically comparing different levels of a variable.

1 Choose **Graph ➤ Boxplot**.

2 In **Y**, enter *Weight*.

3 In **X**, enter *Treatment*.

This tells MINITAB to produce a separate boxplot of weight for each treatment.

4 Click **OK**.

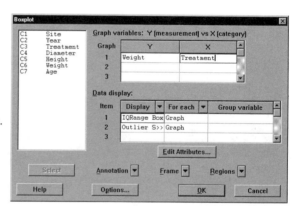

*Graph
window
output*

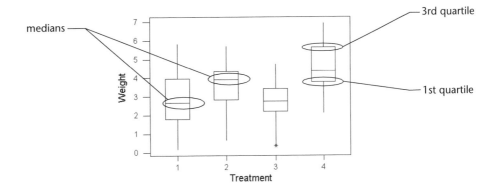

The line drawn across each box indicates the median, or middle, of the data. The bottom and top edges of the box mark the first (25th percentile) and third (75th percentile) quartiles, respectively.

The boxplots suggest that Treatments 2 and 4 (fertilizer and fertilizer/irrigation) have produced the heaviest trees, while Treatments 1 and 3 (control and irrigation) have yielded lighter trees.

You might also expect the site to have an impact on weight. The Site 1 trees planted in the rich, well-drained soil would be expected to weigh more than the Site 2 trees planted in the dry, sandy soil. You can determine if this assumption is true by looking at a boxplot of weight for each site.

Rather than repeat your previous menu selection from the beginning, recall the last Boxplot dialog box and change the X, or category, variable.

5 Choose **Edit ➤ Edit Last Dialog**, or press Ctrl+E.

6 In **X**, enter *Site*.

7 Click **OK**.

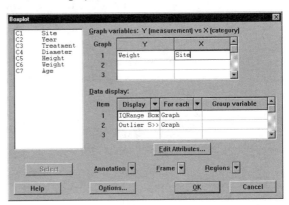

Graph window output

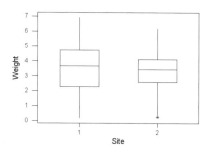

Surprisingly, the Site 1 tree weights do not seem very different from the Site 2 tree weights. The spreads are different for each site, but the medians are almost the same.

Step 9: Perform an Analysis of Variance

You have seen from the boxplots that poplar weights differ noticeably among the four treatments, but not as noticeably between the two sites. Now you decide to use analysis of variance to see if there are statistically significant differences in weight due to the different levels of the factors site and treatment.

When you have two or more factors, MINITAB gives you a choice between balanced ANOVA and the general linear model (GLM). Balanced ANOVA requires a balanced design, that is, you must have the same number of observations for each site/treatment combination. Because your design is not balanced, you will use the general linear model.

1   Choose **Stat ➤ ANOVA ➤ General Linear Model**.

2   In **Responses**, enter *Weight*.

Next, you will enter the model you want GLM to fit. You decide to look at a model with Site, Treatment, and the Site*Treatment interaction.

3   In **Model**, type *Site | Treatment*.

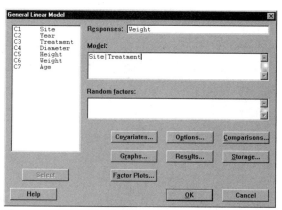

The vertical bar tells MINITAB that you want to include all possible interactions in the model. To make a vertical bar on most keyboards, press (Shift)+(\), or you can use the symbol ! instead.

4 Click **OK**.

Session
window
output

Results for: 4YROLDS.MTW

General Linear Model: Weight versus Site, Treatment

```
Factor      Type Levels Values
Site        fixed    2  1 2
Treatmen    fixed    4  1 2 3 4
```

Analysis of Variance for Weight, using Adjusted SS for Tests

```
Source         DF    Seq SS    Adj SS    Adj MS      F      P
Site            1     3.112     2.424     2.424   1.52  0.219
Treatmen        3    78.005    78.275    26.092  16.39  0.000
Site*Treatmen   3    10.509    10.509     3.503   2.20  0.091
Error         140   222.873   222.873     1.592
Total         147   314.498
```

Unusual Observations for Weight

```
Obs    Weight       Fit    SE Fit  Residual   St Resid
 22   0.35000   2.91200   0.28213  -2.56200     -2.08R
 42   0.64000   3.34167   0.29739  -2.70167     -2.20R
 43   0.16000   3.34167   0.29739  -3.18167     -2.59R
 52   0.66000   3.52250   0.28213  -2.86250     -2.33R
 64   2.36000   4.90889   0.29739  -2.54889     -2.08R
 69   2.12000   4.90889   0.29739  -2.78889     -2.27R
 72   5.82000   3.34167   0.29739   2.47833      2.02R
```

R denotes an observation with a large standardized residual.

GLM lists each factor in the model and the number of levels in each factor. Next GLM lists the analysis of variance table, and finally, it lists unusual observations.

Suppose you want to perform an F-test for each effect in the model. For example, to test the null hypothesis that the treatment effect is the same for both sites (the Site * Treatment interaction), compare MINITAB's p-value with the commonly used α level of 0.05. Because the p-value is 0.091 (a value larger than 0.05) you cannot reject the null hypothesis. That is, you cannot conclude that the treatment effect differs for the two sites.

Now you can look at the main effects, Site and Treatment. The Site p-value of 0.219 is also larger than 0.05, so you cannot conclude that poplar weights differ significantly between the two sites. The p-value for Treatment is small (0.000) thereby supporting the conclusion that mean weights do differ significantly for different treatments.

This agrees with what you saw earlier in the boxplots—that poplar weights were different for different treatments, but only varied slightly between the two sites. Before you decide that Treatment is the only important factor influencing poplar weight, take a look at the Year effect—remember that the researchers planted half the trees in Year 1 and half in Year 2.

Step 10: Compare Weight by Year with Boxplots

You decide to look at a boxplot to compare the weight of poplars planted in Year 1 with those planted in Year 2.

1 Choose **Graph ➤ Boxplot**.

2 In **Y**, enter *Weight*.

3 In **X**, enter *Year*.

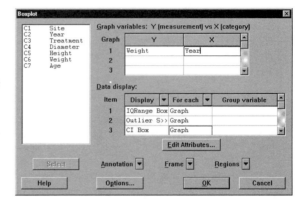

This says to draw a separate boxplot of weight for each year.

Notice the first two rows of the **Data display** table. **IQRange Box** instructs MINITAB to display a box showing the interquartile range, from the 25th to the 75th percentile. **Outlier Symbol** instructs MINITAB to display an asterisk (∗) for all outlier values. You decide to also display a confidence interval box within the IQ Range Box.

4 In the **Data display** table, in the **Display** column, click in the row for item 3.

5 Click the down arrow beside **Display**, and choose **CI Box**.

6 Click in the next cell to the right.

7 Click the down arrow beside **For each** and choose **Graph**.

This row tells MINITAB to include a confidence interval on each boxplot.

By default, MINITAB draws boxplots vertically, but you also can draw them horizontally.

8 Click **Options**.

9 Check **Transpose X and Y**, then click **OK** in each dialog box.

Graph window output

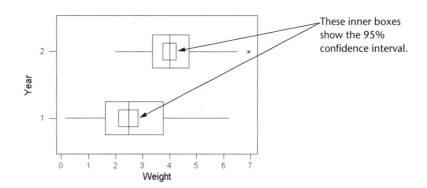

These inner boxes show the 95% confidence interval.

The inner boxes show a 95% confidence interval for the median. The boxplot suggests that poplars planted in Year 2 are heavier than those planted in Year 1. But why is year important? Trees were planted in two different years simply to replicate the data.

You interview the field researchers and learn that they did not apply herbicides to control weeds during the first year planting. As a result, many young trees either died or were severely stunted. To improve the trees' ability to survive, researchers did apply herbicides when they planted poplars the second year.

You draw three preliminary conclusions from your analysis. One, fertilization appears to be an effective way to maximize the weight of poplar clones. Two, it is important to control weeds while the trees are very young. Three, given proper planting and nutrient conditions, poplar clones may not require a high-quality site in order to yield a substantial amount of biomass.

Not only were the Year 2 trees heavier, their weights were more consistent. But before you recommend the use of herbicides and fertilizers, you want to look more closely at the Year 2 trees.

Specifically, you want to know if you still see Site and Treatment effects, when you look at the Year 2 trees alone.

Step 11: Quickly Repeat the Entire Analysis

You decide to repeat the analysis on Year 2 trees only. First, you need to create this subset by splitting the data you just used for the four-year-old trees. Then, rather than redoing all the dialog boxes to repeat the analysis, you will use MINITAB's Command Line Editor.

Split the 4YROLDS worksheet using the values of Year

1 Make sure the Data window named 4YROLDS.MTW is active. To make a Data window active, click on it, or choose its name from the Window menu.

2 Choose **Manip ➤ Split Worksheet**.

3 In **By variables**, enter *Year*. Click **OK**.

Rename the worksheet that contains the data for the Year 2 trees

1 Press Ctrl+I.

2 In the left pane of the Project Manager, right-click on **4YROLDS.MTW(Year = 2)**.

3 Choose **Rename**.

4 Type *YEAR2.MTW*.

5 Press Enter.

Repeat the analysis on the Year 2 trees

1 Make sure the Data window named YEAR2.MTW is active. To make a Data window active, click on it, or choose its name from the Window menu.

2 Press Ctrl+I.

3 In left pane of the Project Manager, click the **History** folder.

The right pane of the Project Manager displays all the commands you have executed in the current project.

4 Scroll through the commands until you find "Histogram."

This was the command you used to check for normality.

5 Click on the Histogram command to select it.

6 Scroll to the bottom of the commands, hold down Shift, and click the last command.

All the commands from Histogram to the end are selected.

7 Choose **Edit ➤ Command Line Editor**, or as a shortcut, press Ctrl+L.

A dialog box appears, containing the MINITAB commands from the section you highlighted.

This dialog box is a simple editor. You can scroll, delete text, type text, and highlight a block of text.

Cut, copy, and paste text using the keyboard: cut with Ctrl+X, copy with Ctrl+C, and paste with Ctrl+V.

8 Click **Submit Commands**.

The entire analysis, a histogram of Weight, boxplots of Weight by Treatment and Weight by Site, an analysis of variance, and a boxplot of Weight by Year are all done, with no further work.

Tip | You can also select consecutive commands in the History folder by clicking and dragging through them. You can select *non*consecutive commands by holding down Ctrl while you click them.

Step 12: Save and Exit

1 Choose **File ➤ Save Project**.

2 In **File name**, enter *POPLAR3* for the name of your project. If you omit the extension .MPJ, MINITAB will automatically add it once you save the project.

3 Click **OK**.

4 If you see a message box asking if you want to replace an existing file, click **Yes**.

5 If you want to take a break at this point, you can exit MINITAB by choosing **File ➤ Exit**, or you can go on to Session Four.

11

Session Four: Quality Control and Improvement

Overview of Session Four

The story

You work for an automobile manufacturer in a department that assembles engines. One of the parts, a camshaft, must be 600 mm ±2 mm long to meet engineering specifications. There has been a chronic problem with camshaft length being out of specification—a problem which has caused poor-fitting assemblies down the production line and high scrap and rework rates.

Your supervisor wants to run $\overline{X}$ and R charts to monitor this characteristic. For a month, data are collected on the length of five camshafts per shift (1 sample of size 5 per shift). You have been asked to lead a problem-solving team and recommend a solution.

What you will learn

In this session you will learn how to:

- produce $\overline{X}$ and R charts

- produce histograms with normal curves

- perform a process capability analysis

Time required

About 30 minutes.

Step 1: Start a New Project

- If you are not already running MINITAB, start the program.

- If you have just completed Session Three, start a new project: choose **File ➤ New**, click **Minitab Project**, then click **OK**.

If you have not saved your changes to the previous project, MINITAB will give you the chance to do so.

Step 2: Open a Worksheet

You will get data from a MINITAB saved worksheet named CAMSHAFT.MTW that is located in the Data subdirectory or folder.

1 Choose **File ➤ Open Worksheet**.

2 Move to the Data subdirectory and select the file CAMSHAFT.MTW. Click **OK**.

3 If it is not visible, open the Data window by pressing [Ctrl]+[D].

The Data window shows you the columns of data in detail.

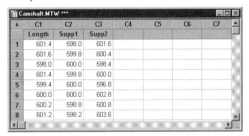

This worksheet contains the results of the sampling plan from the last month. For now, you are concerned with the first column, Length, which contains 100 observations (20 samples of 5 camshafts each). Recall that the camshaft lengths are measured in millimeters.

Step 3: Examine Ranges with an R Chart

First, you want to produce a control chart to look at the range of camshaft lengths within the sample subgroups. You hope that the plotted points fall inside the control limits in a random manner.

1 Choose **Stat ➤ Control Charts ➤ R**.

2 Choose **Single column** and enter *Length*.

3 In **Subgroup size**, type 5.

4 Click **OK**.

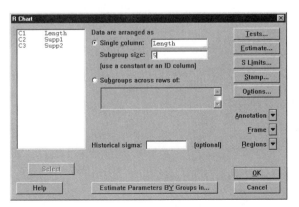

Graph window output

Each point represents a subgroup range (the highest value minus the lowest value in the subgroup).

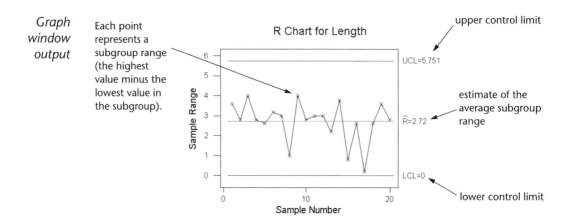

The R chart for Length does not show any points out of control.

Step 4: Test for Special Causes with an Xbar Chart

You will create an $\overline{X}$ chart to see if there is a problem with camshaft lengths being outside acceptable limits. In addition, you will instruct MINITAB to use eight common tests that point out special causes for variation.

1 Choose **Stat ➤ Control Charts ➤ Xbar**.

2 Choose **Single column** and enter *Length*.

3 In **Subgroup size**, type 5.

4 Click **Tests**.

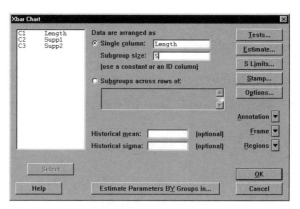

The Tests subdialog box appears.

5 Check **Perform all eight tests**.

6 Click **OK** in each dialog box.

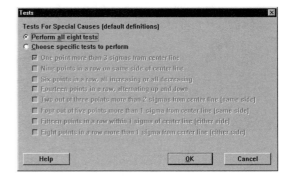

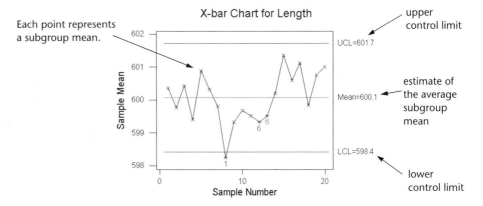

Graph window output

The $\overline{X}$ chart shows that the process is out of control. Specifically, one point has failed test 1, and two points have failed test 6. To find out what these tests mean, look in the Session window.

7 Choose **Window ➤ Session**.

Session window output

```
TEST 1. One point more than 3.00 sigmas from center line.
Test Failed at points: 8
TEST 6. 4 out of 5 points more than 1 sigma from center line
        (on one side of CL).
Test Failed at points: 12 13
```

The process produced one point more than 3 sigmas from the center line, and four of five points more than 1 sigma from the center line (on one side of the center line).

Now that you have confirmed that a problem does exist, it is time to look for causes and solutions. Unfortunately, the sampling plan did not allow for detailed inspection of precisely where and when the problems occurred because only one sample was taken per shift. A better plan would have been to take multiple samples per shift for the troubleshooting phase, and to switch to this monitoring plan after special causes were found and eliminated. Nonetheless, you are determined to get what you can out of the data that you have.

Step 5: Create a Histogram with Normal Curve

The histogram with normal curve is useful for examining a variable's distribution. You decide to examine the variable Length.

1 Choose **Stat ➤ Basic Statistics ➤ Display Descriptive Statistics**.

2 In **Variables**, enter *Length*.

3 Click **Graphs**.

The Graphs subdialog box appears.

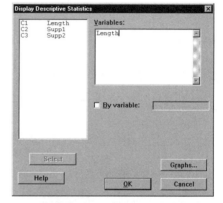

4 Check **Histogram of data, with normal curve**.

5 Click **OK** in each dialog box.

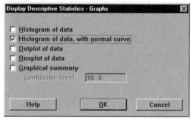

Graph window output

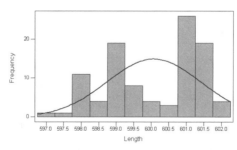

Histogram of Length, with Normal Curve

In general, we expect a variable such as Length to follow the normal distribution. In this case, the histogram would be approximately bell-shaped. The histogram you just created is certainly not bell-shaped. In fact, it would appear from the spikes at 598, 599, and 601 that we may be dealing with more than one separate and distinct distributions.

An examination of the inventory records indicates that there are two suppliers for the camshafts. Now you are starting to understand the odd histogram. You decide to obtain measurements from both suppliers and run $\overline{X}$ and R charts separately on each set of data with a subgroup size of 5 for each. The data for each supplier are stored in the columns Supp1 and Supp2 of your worksheet.

Step 6: Display Combined Xbar and R Charts

Your worksheet contains variables named Supp1 and Supp2 with data for Suppliers 1 and 2. You could repeat the same procedures to produce control charts for Supplier 1 as you did to produce the charts for Length. However, there is another command, Xbar-R, that you can use to display both charts together.

More | The Xbar-R command is actually a macro—a collection of MINITAB commands that are executed as a single command. You can use macros to automate repetitive tasks as well as to create your own custom MINITAB feature.

1 Choose **Stat ➤ Control Charts ➤ Xbar-R**.

2 Choose **Single column** and enter *Supp1*.

3 In **Subgroup size**, type 5. Click **OK**.

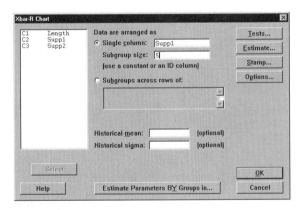

Graph window output

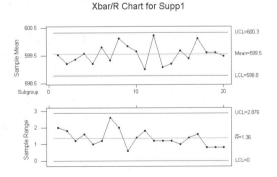

Xbar/R Chart for Supp1

Both the means and ranges for Supplier 1 appear to be in control, although you notice that the mean is 599.5 mm, not 600. The average range for Supplier 1 is 1.36 mm.

Evaluate Supplier 2

You can produce the same control charts for Supplier 2, using the variable named Supp2, as you did for Supplier 1.

1 Press [Ctrl]+[E].

This keyboard shortcut, for **Edit ➤ Edit Last Dialog**, brings up the Xbar-R Chart dialog box again.

2 In **Single column**, enter *Supp2*. Click **OK**.

You do not need to enter a subgroup size because it was still set to 5 from the last time you used this dialog box. MINITAB "remembers" the dialog box settings from the last time a dialog box was used in a session.

Graph window output

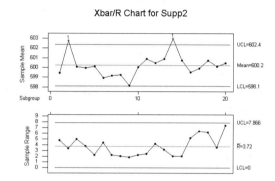

Supplier 2's $\overline{X}$ chart reveals problems. From the chart, you can see that two points are above the upper control limit.

The R chart does not indicate that the process is out of control. However, you notice that the center line is at 3.72, which is almost three times larger than Supplier 1's $\overline{R}$ of 1.36.

As team leader, you recommend that longer production runs be accepted from Supplier 1 until Supplier 2 can demonstrate that camshaft production is in control. You will work with Supplier 2 to reduce process variability to an acceptable level. Because of the statistical evidence to support your position, your recommendation is implemented.

Step 7: Prepare for a Process Capability Analysis

So now you have managed to reduce variability by using only Supplier 1. The number of poor-quality assemblies being produced down the line has dropped significantly, but problems have not completely disappeared. You decide to run a capability study to see whether Supplier 1 alone is capable of meeting your engineering specifications of 600 mm ±2 mm.

Before you can proceed with capability analysis, the process must be in control. The control charts have shown that, thanks to your recommendation, the process is now in control. You also expect the camshaft lengths to be normally distributed. Now you want to view a histogram to check normality.

First you want to look at the distribution of camshaft lengths for Supplier 1:

1 Choose **Stat ➤ Basic Statistics ➤ Display Descriptive Statistics**.

2 In **Variables**, enter *Supp1*. Click **OK**.

Graph window output

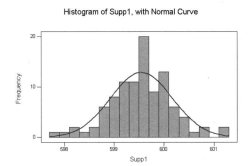

Histogram of Supp1, with Normal Curve

MINITAB produces a histogram with normal curve again, based on your earlier selections.

You are satisfied by the bell shape of the distribution, and you do not see multiple modes or peaks as you did earlier.

You are ready to proceed.

Step 8: Perform a Process Capability Analysis

Now you are ready to run a process capability analysis to see if Supplier 1 is capable of meeting your engineering specifications of 600 mm ±2 mm.

1 Choose **Stat ➤ Quality Tools ➤ Capability Analysis (Normal)**.

2 Choose **Single column** and enter *Supp1*.

3 In **Subgroup size**, type 5.

Next, enter the specification limits.

4 In **Lower spec**, type 598.

5 In **Upper spec**, type 602.

6 Click **Options**.

7 In **Target (adds Cpm to table)**, type 600.

8 Click **OK** in each dialog box.

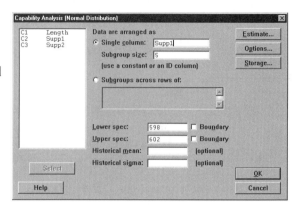

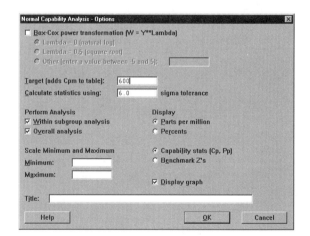

Graph window output

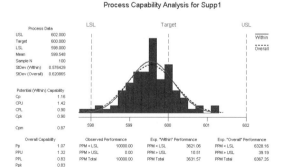

From the graph you can see that the process mean falls short of the target and the process distribution mean lies to the left of the target. Also, the left tail of the distribution falls outside the lower specification limit. Therefore, some camshafts will not meet the lower specification of 598 mm.

The Capability Analysis command also produces a table of statistics. The Cpk index indicates whether the process will produce units within the tolerance limits. A Cpk index of 1 means that a process is exactly capable of meeting specifications, while less than 1 means that the process is not meeting specification limits. Ideally, you would like to see a Cpk much larger than 1, because the larger the index, the more capable the process. The Cpk index for Supplier 1 is only 0.90, indicating that they need to improve by reducing variability and by centering the process around the target.

Since Supplier 1 is currently your best supplier of camshafts, you will work with them to improve their process and, therefore, your own. MINITAB offers analysis of variance (ANOVA), regression, design of experiments (DOE), and many other statistical tools that you will use to continuously improve your processes.

Step 9: Save and Exit

1 Choose **File ➤ Save Project**.

2 In **File name**, enter *CAMSHFT1* for the name of your project. If you omit the extension .MPJ, MINITAB will automatically add it once you save the project.

3 Click **OK**.

4 If you see a message box asking if you want to replace an existing file, click **Yes**.

5 If you want to take a break at this point, you can exit MINITAB by choosing **File ➤ Exit**, or you can go on to Session Five.

12

Session Five: Designing an Experiment

Overview of Session Five

The story

For this lesson, assume that you work at a chemical plant. You are studying one of the reactions that produces a chemical product. You would like some way to increase the yield of a product that is produced from the reaction. From past experience, you have seen that varying the temperature, the pressure, and the type of catalyst seems to change the yield of the reaction. A problem is that everyone you work with has their own theory about how each of these factors affects the reaction. You want to make real improvements, so you decide to run an experiment to determine the actual effects of the three factors.

What you will learn

In Session Five, you will learn how to:

■ design a factorial experiment to tell which factors are important to the reaction

■ fit a full model to the data

■ use several simple graphical methods to help determine which effects are active (important) or inactive

■ fit a reduced model to the data, and then assess the adequacy of the model

Time required

About 30 minutes.

Step 1: Start a New Project

■ If you are not already running MINITAB, start the program.

■ If you have just completed Session Four, start a new project: choose **File ➤ New**, click **Minitab Project**, then click **OK**.

If you have not saved your changes to the previous project, MINITAB will give you the chance to do so.

Step 2: Create the Experimental Design

Select a design

Suppose you want to design an experiment to test three factors: time, temperature, and type of catalyst.

1 Choose **Stat ➤ DOE ➤ Factorial ➤ Create Factorial Design**.

Only two buttons are enabled, **Display Available Designs** and **Designs**. The other buttons are for setting levels of factors, specifying options, and controlling the Session window output. MINITAB enables these buttons after you have chosen your design.

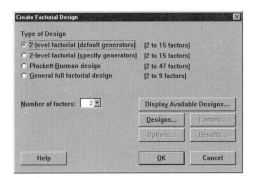

2 Click **Display Available Designs**.

Use this table to help you select an appropriate design, based on:

- the number of factors that are of interest,

- the number of runs you can afford in the experiment, and

- the desired resolution of the design.

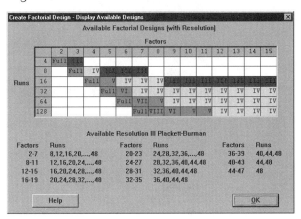

Since you have three factors that are of interest, you can see in the table that you have two options. You can choose

- a fractional factorial design of resolution III with 4 runs, or

- a full factorial design with 8 runs

A two-level design with three factors has 2^3 (or eight) possible factor combinations. By choosing a design with all possible combinations, called a full factorial design, you will get results that show effects free from confounding, that is, all effects are distinguishable from other effects. However, you may also be able to obtain meaningful results by doing fewer runs or combinations. Designs that use less than all possible combinations are called fractional factorial designs.

You decide that the full factorial design with 3 factors and 8 runs is more appropriate than the fractional factorial design. At your chemical plant, runs that manipulate the factors of interest—time, temperature, and type of catalyst—are not expensive or time-consuming. Also, the experiment can be performed at a non-peak period without disturbing the workflow at the plant. If the runs of the experiment were costly or difficult to perform, you may have made a different decision.

3   Click **OK**. You are now back in the main dialog box.

4   Choose **2-level factorial (default generators)**.

5   In **Number of factors**, choose 3.

6   Click **Designs**.

The box at the top shows all available designs for the design type and number of factors you selected.

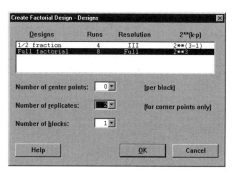

7   In the **Designs** box, select **Full factorial**.

8   In **Number of replicates**, choose 2.

9   Click **OK**. This selects the design and brings you back to the main dialog box. Notice that the remaining buttons are now enabled.

Name factors and set factor levels

You can enter factor levels (settings) as numeric or text. If your factors could be *continuous*, use numeric levels; if your factors are *categorical*, use text levels. Continuous variables can take on any value on the measurement scale being used (for example, length of reaction time). In contrast, categorical variable can only assume a limited number of possible values (for example, type of catalyst).

You now need to choose settings for your factors. In a two-level factorial design, you set factors at two levels. Many experimenters advocate choosing limits as far apart as possible (within limits of safety if you know them). After some deliberation, you choose the following settings:

Factor	Low Setting	High Setting
Temperature	20° C	40° C
Pressure	1 atmosphere	4 atmospheres
Catalyst	A	B

Create the Experimental Design

Session Five: Designing an Experiment

1 Click **Factors**.

2 Click on the first row of the **Name** column to change the name of the first factor. Then, use the arrow keys to navigate within the table, moving across rows or down columns. In the row for:

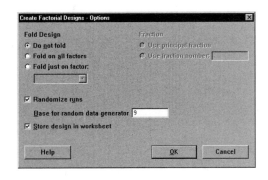

- **Factor** A, type *Temp* in **Name**, *20* in **Low**, and *40* in **High**.

- **Factor** B, type *Pressure* in **Name**, *1* in **Low**, and *4* in **High**.

- **Factor** C, type *Catalyst* in **Name**, A in **Low**, and B in **High**.

3 Click **OK**. This brings you back to the main dialog box.

More | If you have a design that includes center points and you have both numeric and text factors, you need to be aware that there really is no true center to the design. In this case, center points are called pseudo-center points. See Help or Chapter 19, *Factorial Designs* in MINITAB *User's Guide 2* for a discussion of pseudo-center points.

Randomize and store the design

1 Click **Options**.

2 In **Base for random data generator**, type *9*.

Entering a base for the random data generator allows you to control the randomization so that you obtain the same pattern every time. This way you will get the same design order that is used in this sample session.

3 Make sure **Store design in worksheet** is checked. Click **OK**.

4 You are now back in the main dialog box. Click **OK**. This will generate the design and store the design in the worksheet.

Tip | It is usually a good idea to randomize the run order. Randomizing the order of the runs lessens the effects of other factors that are not included in the study, particularly effects that are time-dependent.

Step 3: View the Design

Open the Data window so you can see what the structure of a typical design looks like.

1 Choose **Window ➤ Worksheet 1,** or as a shortcut, press Ctrl+D.

The Data window should now look like this:

	C1	C2	C3	C4	C5	C6	C7-T
	StdOrder	RunOrder	CenterPt	Blocks	Temp	Pressure	Catalyst
1	2	1	1	1	40	1	A
2	14	2	1	1	40	1	B
3	4	3	1	1	40	4	A
4	3	4	1	1	20	4	A
5	1	5	1	1	20	1	A
6	16	6	1	1	40	4	B
7	11	7	1	1	20	4	A

Notice the columns named StdOrder (C1) and RunOrder (C2). Every time you create a design, MINITAB reserves C1 and C2 to store the standard order and run order.

- StdOrder shows what the order of the runs in the experiment would be if the experiment was done in standard, or Yates', order.

- RunOrder shows what the order of the runs in the experiment would be if the experiment was run in random order.

If you do not randomize a design, the standard order and run order are the same.

In addition, MINITAB stores the center point indicators in C3 and the block numbers in C4. Since you did not add center points or block the design, MINITAB sets all the values in C3 and C4 to one.

Next in the worksheet are the factor columns, beginning with C5. In this example, the factors are in C5 through C7. Since you entered the factor levels in the Factors subdialog box, you see the actual levels in the worksheet.

More | You can use **Stat ➤ DOE ➤ Display Design** to switch back and forth between a random and standard order display, and between a coded and uncoded display in the worksheet.

There are two ways to change the factor settings or names: use **Stat ➤ DOE ➤ Modify Design,** or type new factor names directly in the Data window.

Step 4: Collect and Enter Data in the Worksheet

At this point, you may want to create a data collection form for your experiment. Print the Data window with its grid lines.

1 In the Data window, click on the name field of C8 and type *Yield*.

2 Choose **File ➤ Print Worksheet**, and make sure **Print Grid Lines** is checked. Click **OK**.

Now you would perform all sixteen runs of the experiment, and record the observed yields. Suppose you came up with the following product yields (in grams):

66 66 102 98 65 54 107 68 53 66 55 85 108 89 52 63

3 Type the observed yields into the Yield column of the Data window.

Step 5: Screen the Design

When you screen a design, the object is to select factors that have large effects. Now that you have created a factorial design and collected the response data, you can fit a model to the results and generate some graphs to evaluate the effects. You will use the output from fitting a mathematical model, and you will also use two graphical methods to help see which factors are important for improving the yield in the reaction.

Fit a model

Since you have created and stored a factorial design, you will notice that MINITAB has enabled the **DOE ➤ Factorial** menu commands **Analyze Factorial Design** and **Factorial Plots**. If you plot the responses rather than the fitted values (least-squares means), you can generate main effects plots, interaction plots, and cube plots either before or after you actually fit a model. In this sample session, you will fit the model first.

1 Choose **Stat ➤ DOE ➤ Factorial ➤ Analyze Factorial Design**.

2 In **Responses**, enter *Yield*.

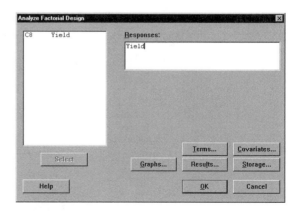

3 Click **Graphs**.

4 To generate two effects plots
   that will help you determine
   which effects are active,
   check **Normal** and **Pareto**.
   Use the default α level (0.10).

5 Click **OK**. This brings you
   back to the main dialog box.

Now you have selected the
model you want to fit, the graphs
you want to display, and you
have set all other options.

6 To display the requested
   output in the Session window, and each graph in a separate Graph window, click
   OK in the main dialog box.

Identify important effects

You can use both the Session window output and the two effects plots to help you
decide which effects are important to your process. First, you will look at the Session
window output.

*Session
window
output*

Fractional Factorial Fit: Yield versus Temp, Pressure, Catalyst

Estimated Effects and Coefficients for Yield (coded units)

Term	Effect	Coef	SE Coef	T	P
Constant		74.81	2.561	29.21	0.000
Temp	1.38	0.69	2.561	0.27	0.795
Pressure	14.12	7.06	2.561	2.76	0.025
Catalyst	-30.38	-15.19	2.561	-5.93	0.000
Temp*Pressure	-0.13	-0.06	2.561	-0.02	0.981
Temp*Catalyst	-1.13	-0.56	2.561	-0.22	0.832
Pressure*Catalyst	-13.37	-6.69	2.561	-2.61	0.031
Temp*Pressure*Catalyst	-0.13	-0.06	2.561	-0.02	0.981

Analysis of Variance for Yield (coded units)

Source	DF	Seq SS	Adj SS	Adj MS	F	P
Main Effects	3	4496.19	4496.19	1498.73	14.28	0.001
2-Way Interactions	3	720.69	720.69	240.23	2.29	0.155
3-Way Interactions	1	0.06	0.06	0.06	0.00	0.981
Residual Error	8	839.50	839.50	104.94		
Pure Error	8	839.50	839.50	104.94		
Total	15	6056.44				

```
Estimated Coefficients for Yield using data in uncoded units

Term                           Coef
Constant                     60.6667
Temp                        0.079167
Pressure                     4.83333
Catalyst                     -2.6667
Temp*Pressure              -0.004167
Temp*Catalyst              -0.045833
Pressure*Catalyst           -4.33333
Temp*Pressure*Catalyst     -0.004167
```

You fit the full model, which includes the three main effects, three two-way
interactions, and one three-way interaction. Use the values in the P column of the
Estimated Effects and Coefficients table to determine which of the effects are
significant. Using $\alpha = 0.05$, the main effects for Pressure and Catalyst, and the
Pressure*Catalyst interaction are significant; that is, their p-values are less than 0.05.

Effects plots

Now you can use the normal probability plot and the Pareto chart of the effects to see
which effects influence the response, Yield.

Active effects are effects that are significant or important. In the normal plot of the
effects, points that do not fit the line well usually signal active effects. Active effects are
larger and further from the fitted line than inactive effects. Inactive effects tend to be
smaller and centered around zero, the mean of all the effects.

1 To make the normal probability plot appear in the active window, choose **Window**
   ➤ **Effects Plot for Yield**.

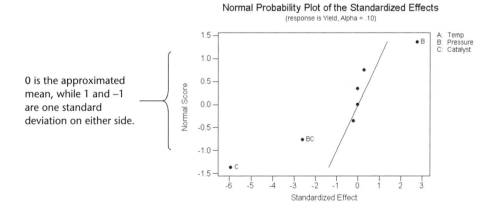

0 is the approximated
mean, while 1 and –1
are one standard
deviation on either side.

The normal probability plot labels effects that are lower than the α level you chose in
the Analyze Factorial Design–Graphs subdialog box. Here, the effects of Pressure,
Catalyst, and the Pressure*Catalyst interaction are significant using $\alpha = 0.10$.

A Pareto chart of the effects is another useful tool that you can use to help determine which effects are active.

2 To make the Pareto chart appear in the active window, choose **Window ➤ Effects Pareto for Yield**.

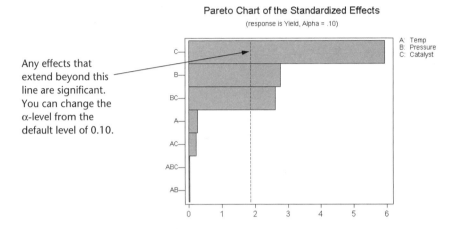

MINITAB displays the absolute value of the effects on the Pareto chart.

The Pareto chart uses the same α as the normal plot to determine the significance of effects. So again, you see that Pressure, Catalyst, and Pressure*Catalyst are significant (α = 0.10).

Later, you will fit a model without the terms Temp, Temp*Pressure, and Temp*Catalyst, which seem to be inactive. You will check to see how good the model is after you fit the reduced model.

Step 6: Fit a Reduced Model

Next, you want to fit a new model using only the terms you identified as important by looking at the results of fitting the full model—in other words, screening out the unimportant effects. After you fit the model, you will generate several plots to visualize the effects, evaluate the fit of the reduced model, and do a residual analysis.

You will fit a model that includes Pressure, Catalyst, and the Pressure*Catalyst interaction.

1 Choose **Stat ➤ DOE ➤ Factorial ➤ Analyze Factorial Design**.

2 Click **Terms**.

3 Set up the model you want to fit.

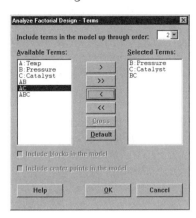

- From **Include terms in the model up through order,** choose **2**. Notice this moves ABC to the **Available Terms** box.

- Click on *A:Temp* in the **Selected Terms** box, then click ◄ . This will move the *A:Temp* variable to the **Available Terms** list box.

- Repeat these actions to move the AB and AC interactions to the **Available Terms** box.

4 Click **OK**. You are now back in the main dialog box.

5 Click **Graphs**. Uncheck **Normal** and **Pareto**.

6 Check **Histogram**, **Normal plot**, **Residuals versus fits**, and **Residuals versus order**. Click **OK** and return to the main dialog box.

7 Click **OK** in the Analyze Factorial Design dialog box.

The output will display in the Session window and the residual plots will display in Graph windows.

Was your choice of active effects a good one? Is your model valid? You will try to answer these questions next when you evaluate the reduced model.

Step 7: Evaluate the Reduced Model

The Session window output provides information as to how good the model is. Examine the P column, which contains p-values for each of the terms in the model. A good standard by which to evaluate the model is to look at p-values. If all terms have p-values less than the α level appropriate for your experiment, you can be confident that you have a good model. Here, you choose to use $\alpha = 0.05$.

Session window output

Fractional Factorial Fit: Yield versus Pressure, Catalyst

These are the p-values for each term in the model.

Estimated Effects and Coefficients for Yield (coded units)

Term	Effect	Coef	SE Coef	T	P
Constant		74.81	2.107	35.51	0.000
Pressure	14.13	7.06	2.107	3.35	0.006
Catalyst	-30.37	-15.19	2.107	-7.21	0.000
Pressure*Catalyst	-13.38	-6.69	2.107	-3.17	0.008

Analysis of Variance for Yield (coded units)

Source	DF	Seq SS	Adj SS	Adj MS	F	P
Main Effects	2	4488.62	4488.62	2244.31	31.60	0.000
2-Way Interactions	1	715.56	715.56	715.56	10.08	0.008
Residual Error	12	852.25	852.25	71.02		
Pure Error	12	852.25	852.25	71.02		
Total	15	6056.44				

Estimated Coefficients for Yield using data in uncoded units

Term	Coef
Constant	63.0417
Pressure	4.70833
Catalyst	-4.04167
Pressure*Catalyst	-4.45833

The p-value for each term in the model is less than 0.05, indicating a model that is a good candidate for further exploration and validation. This model is considerably simpler and fits the data almost as well as the model with all terms. The residual error only increased by a small amount.

You can further check the model by using the residual plots. The fitted values are the results predicted by your model. The residuals are the actual yields minus the predicted yields. The following graphs display:

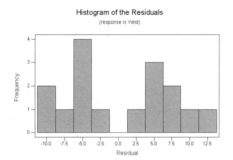

This is a reasonably good normal plot.

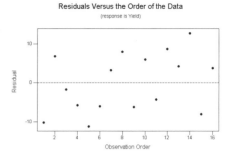

There is a good spread of points on either side of zero, with no patterns of increase or decrease.

Although this histogram does not appear to represent a normal distribution, there is not enough information to make a judgement. It is very difficult to interpret a histogram with only 16 plotted points.

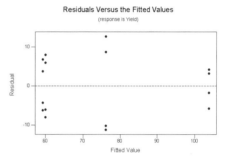

This plot shows a reasonable pattern of dispersion. But again, it is difficult to interpret a plot with only 16 points.

The residuals plots were satisfactory, and showed no cause for concern.

Step 8: Draw Conclusions

Display the factorial plots

Now generate two graphs that will allow you to visualize the effects—a main effects plot and an interactions plot. When the plots are based on the means of the response data, you can generate them either before or after you actually fit a model to the data. When you are plotting the fitted values (least-squares means), you need to fit the model first.

1   Choose **Stat ➤ DOE ➤ Factorial ➤ Factorial Plots**.

2   Check **Main effects** and click **Setup**.

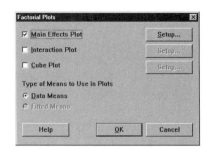

3   In **Responses**, type *Yield*.

4   Next, select the terms you want to plot:

   ■   Click on *B:Pressure* in the **Available** box, then click on the single arrow that points to the right. This will move the *B:Pressure* variable to the **Selected** box.

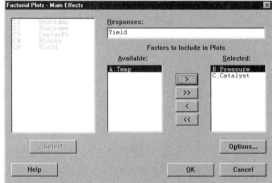

   ■   Repeat these actions to move *C:Catalyst* to the **Selected** box. Click **OK**.

5   Check **Interaction** and click **Setup**.

6   Repeat steps 3 and 4.

7   Click **OK** in the main Factorial Plots dialog box to display each plot in a separate Graph window.

Evaluate the plots

First, take a look at a plot that shows the basic effect of changing pressure, or using catalyst A versus catalyst B. These one-factor effects are called *main effects*. In Step 7 (page 12-11), you displayed the numerical values for all the effects in the Session window.

1   Choose **Window ➤ Main Effects for Yield** to make the main effects plot the active window:

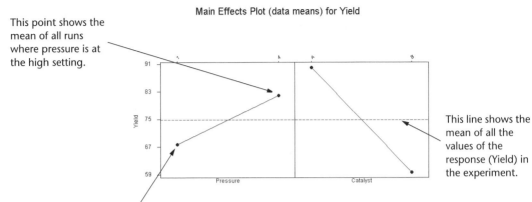

This point shows the mean of all runs where pressure is at the high setting.

This line shows the mean of all the values of the response (Yield) in the experiment.

This point shows the mean of all runs where pressure is at the low setting.

Two main effects plots display in this graph—one for pressure and one for catalyst. The *main effect* of:

- pressure is the difference between the low setting and the high setting on the graph

- catalyst is the difference between the two categories

You can see that the type of catalyst has a bigger main effect than pressure. That is, the line connecting the mean responses for catalyst A and catalyst B has a steeper slope than the line connecting the mean responses at the low and high settings of pressure. Although the type of catalyst appears to affect the Yield more than pressure, it is very important to look at the interaction. An interaction can magnify or cancel out a main effect.

To calculate main effects, MINITAB subtracts the mean response at the low or first level of the factor from the mean response at the high or second level of the factor. The table below summarizes the findings:

Factor	Size of Effect	Interpretation
Pressure	+14.13	runs at 4 atmospheres of pressure had higher yields than runs at 1 atmosphere of pressure
Catalyst	−30.37	runs that used catalyst A had higher yields than runs that used catalyst B

If you have no interactions between the factors, this graph will adequately describe where you can get the biggest payoff for changes in your factors.

The next step, then, is to look at the significant interaction. Although you have already verified a significant interaction with the Session window output, you can look at the interaction plot to see how big this effect is.

2 To make the interaction plot the active window, choose **Window ➤ Interaction Plot for Yield**.

The vertical scale (y-axis) is in units of the response variable (here the response variable is Yield).

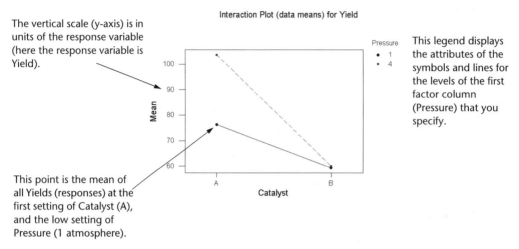

Interaction Plot (data means) for Yield

This legend displays the attributes of the symbols and lines for the levels of the first factor column (Pressure) that you specify.

This point is the mean of all Yields (responses) at the first setting of Catalyst (A), and the low setting of Pressure (1 atmosphere).

The horizontal scale (x-axis) shows the levels of the second factor column (Catalyst) that you specify.

An interaction plot shows the impact that changing the settings of one factor has on another factor. Because an interaction can magnify or diminish main effects, evaluating interactions is extremely important. The significant interaction between pressure and catalyst shows up as two lines with sharply differing slopes.

The yields for catalyst A are greater than yields for catalyst B at both 1 and 4 atmospheres of pressure. However, you can see that the difference in yields between runs using catalyst A and runs using catalyst B at 4 atmospheres is much greater than the difference in yields between runs using catalyst A and runs using catalyst B at 1 atmosphere.

In order to get the highest yield for your experiment, your results suggest that you should set pressure to 4 atmospheres and use catalyst A.

Step 9: Save and Exit

1 Choose **File ➤ Save Project**.

2 In **File name**, enter *SS5DOE* for the name of your project. If you omit the extension .MPJ, MINITAB will automatically add it once you save the project.

3 Click **Save**.

4 If you see a message box asking if you want to replace an existing file, click **Yes**.

5 To close MINITAB, choose **File ➤ Exit**.

Step 10: What You Learned

So, that is the end of your analysis! Let's summarize what you did:

1 You decided on a design for the experiment, then generated and saved settings using the Create Factorial Design command.

2 You ran the experiment and entered the responses.

3 You fit the full model to look at some numerical values and generated two effects plots to see which terms seemed to be active.

4 You screened out unimportant effects, then fit a reduced model.

5 You generated main effects and interactions plots with the Factorial Plots command to visualize the effects.

6 You evaluated the reduced model with the p-values in the Analyze Factorial Design output and the various residuals plot.

You could have used additional analysis techniques in MINITAB as well.

Let's summarize what you have learned:

■ From looking at the effects plots, you determined that pressure, type of catalyst, and the interaction between pressure and catalyst were active. Evaluating interactions is extremely important, because an interaction can magnify or cancel out main effects.

■ You can eliminate (screen out) the other terms without significantly affecting predictions.

■ Now that you have a model to predict the yield, you can apply this model to help obtain higher yields in future experiments.

In order to get the highest yield for your experiment, your results suggest that you should:

■ set pressure to 4 atmospheres

■ use Catalyst A

■ evaluate higher levels of pressure with future experiments

All that for 16 runs. Quite a payoff!

References

[1] R.V. Lenth (1989). "Quick and Easy Analysis of Unreplicated Factorials," *Technometrics*, Vol 31, p.469.

INDEX

Numerics

MINITAB Graphics Format (MGF) files 5-11

MINITAB Portable Worksheet (MTP) files 2-10

MINITAB Project (MPJ) files 1-10, 2-10

MINITAB Worksheet (MTW) files 2-10

move to command output 6-2

moving columns 3-5

MPJ (MINITAB Project) files 1-10, 2-10

MTP (MINITAB Portable Worksheet) files 2-10

MTW (MINITAB Worksheet) files 2-10

multivariate analysis 4-2

N

naming
    columns 3-5
    constants 2-3
    matrices 2-3
    worksheets 10-7, 10-14

navigating in the Session window 6-2

new
    projects 9-2
    worksheets 2-6

next command in the Session window 6-2

nonparametric analysis 4-2

normal plot of effects 12-7

normal probability plot 4-10

numeric data 2-2, 3-7

O

object linking and embedding
    see OLE

ODBC (Open Database Connectivity) 2-13

OLE 5-11, 5-12

one-sample confidence interval 4-4

one-sample t-test 4-4

one-way analysis of variance 4-9

Open Database Connectivity (ODBC) 2-13

opening
    graphs 1-13, 5-11
    MINITAB program 8-3
    projects 1-10
    worksheets 1-13, 2-6, 2-10, 2-11, 8-3

operating system, using your 1-2

overview of MINITAB 1-1

P

paired t-test 4-4

Pareto chart of effects 12-7

pasting
    cells 3-4
    data 2-7
    graphs 5-11

patterned data 2-8, 8-4

Pearson correlation coefficient 4-5, 8-10

plots 5-3, 8-9
    fitted regression line 9-8
    residuals 9-7

preferences, saving 1-11

preview
    of a non-MINITAB file 2-11
    of a project file 2-11
    of a worksheet 2-11

previous command in the Session window 6-2

printing 8-11
    Data window 1-15
    files 2-10
    graphs 5-11
    Session window output 6-6, 8-10
    windows 1-15, 8-11

probability distributions 3-15

process capability analysis 11-10

Project Manager 1-4

projects 1-10
    closing 1-10
    descriptions for 1-11
    new 9-2
    opening 1-10
    previewing 2-11
    saving 1-10, 8-5, 8-12

Q

quality control 4-1, 4-12
    see also control charts

quality planning tools 4-1, 4-2, 4-12

querying a database with ODBC 2-13

R

R charts 4-13, 11-3

random data, generating 3-15

randomizing run order 12-4

read-only or editable, making output 6-3

readme file 1-16

recoding data 3-13, 10-5

registering as a MINITAB user xi

regression 4-2, 4-7, 9-3, 9-6
    fitted line plot 9-8
    residual plots 9-4, 9-7

Release 13 capabilities summary xv

reliability/survival analysis 4-2

renaming worksheets 10-7, 10-14

repeating a block of commands 7-3

replacing text in the Session window 6-5

resetting dialog boxes 9-6

residual plots 4-10, 9-4, 9-7, 12-12

retrieving data from a file 8-3

Rich Text Format (RTF) file 6-4

rows, inserting 3-4

RTF (Rich Text Format) file 6-4

opening 1-13, 2-11, 8-3
previewing 2-11
renaming 10-7, 10-14
saving 2-10
splitting 3-11, 10-6, 10-14
Worksheet folder 2-4
WWW address xii, 1-17

X

Xbar charts 4-13, 11-4
Xbar-R charts 4-13, 11-7

Z

Z-test 4-4

How to Order Additional Products

To order, contact Minitab Inc. between 8:00 a.m. and 5:30 p.m. Eastern time, Monday through Friday, or contact Minitab Ltd., Minitab SARL, or your distributor. If you are calling Minitab Inc. from within the USA or Canada, call 800-448-3555. Otherwise, call (+1) 814-238-3280, or contact Minitab Inc. via e-mail at sales@minitab.com. Contact information for Minitab Ltd (UK only: 0800 0929 353) and Minitab SARL (France only: 0800 608440) are provided on the back cover of this book. Or, visit our web site at http://www.minitab.com.

Additional Documentation

Minitab Inc. offers clearly-written documentation to assist MINITAB users in installing, running, and applying MINITAB functionality to statistical problem solving.

Release 13 for Windows

MINITAB User's Guide 1: Data, Graphics, and Macros

A complete and detailed manual covering data manipulation, file input and output, graphics, and macros commands, with numerous examples throughout.

MINITAB User's Guide 2: Data Analysis and Quality Tools

A complete and detailed manual covering statistics, quality control, reliability and survival analysis, and design of experimentss, with numerous examples throughout.

Meet MINITAB

A concise guide to getting started with MINITAB, including sample sessions, to get you "up and running" quickly.

Older Releases

Documentation for older releases of MINITAB is available. For details, contact Minitab Inc., Minitab Ltd., Minitab SARL, or your distributor.

Any Release

MINITAB Handbook, Third Edition

A supplementary text that teaches basic statistics using MINITAB. The Handbook features the creative use of plots, application of standard statistical methods to real data, in-depth exploration of data, and more.

Additional MINITAB Products

Please contact us if you'd like more information about these products:

- MINITAB Training, on-site and public training designed to save time and money by providing practical, useful information on how best to use MINITAB to optimize your company's performance.
- MINITAB Student, a streamlined and economical version of MINITAB, designed specially for introductory general and business statistics.
- MINITAB in French, a completely localized version of MINITAB.

Older releases of MINITAB are available in Spanish, and in English for several computer platforms including Macintosh, older Windows systems, DOS systems, and Unix workstations.

Minitab Global

Minitab products can be purchased through Minitab Inc., Minitab Ltd., Minitab SARL, or one of Minitab's authorized international partners. From Antarctica to Zimbabwe, Minitab Inc. and its partners are available world-wide to service and support Minitab customers.

For information about the international partner serving your market, please refer to the *International Partners Card* included in your software product box. For additional listings since the time of printing, please visit our web site (http://www.minitab.com), or contact

Minitab Inc. at the USA office (call +1 814.238.3280, fax +1 814.238.4383, or e-mail intlsales@minitab.com);

Minitab Ltd. at the UK office (call +44 (0) 24 7665 2777, fax +44 (0) 24 7665 2888, or e-mail sales@minitab.co.uk); or

Minitab SARL in France (call +33 (0) 1 55 33 12 36, fax +33 (0) 1 55 33 12 39, or e-mail bienvenue@minitab.fr).